HOW TO BECOME A
SEX
GODDESS

HOW TO BECOME A SEX GODDESS

SECRETS OF DIVINE LOVEMAKING

E.M. Lovejoy

D&C
David and Charles

A DAVID & CHARLES BOOK

Copyright © David & Charles Limited 2009

David & Charles is an F+W Media Inc. company
4700 East Galbraith Road
Cincinnati, OH 45236

First published in the USA in 2009 as Sex Goddess
This edition first published in the UK in 2009

Contains material adapted and abridged from His/Hers,
by Nicole Murn and Justin Cord Hayes, copyright © F+W
Media, Inc. 2006; The Everything® Great Sex Book, by Suzie
Heumann and Susan Campbell, PhD, copyright © F+W
Media, Inc. 2004; The Everything® Kama Sutra Book, by Suzie
Heumann, copyright © F+W Media, Inc. 2004

ISBN-13: 978-0-7153-3638-0
ISBN-10: 0-7153-3638-X

Printed in the UK by CPI Antony Rowe
for David & Charles
Brunel House   Newton Abbot   Devon

Visit our website at www.davidandcharles.co.uk

David & Charles books are available from all good book-
shops; alternatively you can contact our Orderline on 0870
9908222 or write to us at FREEPOST EX2 110, D&C Direct,
Newton Abbot, TQ12 4ZZ (no stamp required UK only); US
customers call 800-289-0963 and Canadian customers call
800-840-5220.

CONTENTS

INTRODUCTION

Sex, or the *idea* of it, is everywhere, all around us, and yet most of us know very little about it. Sex sells everything from new cars to aged whiskey, but when it comes down to having it, we often feel confused. Whether we're young or older, many of us feel that society sends mixed messages about sexuality.

Exploring and learning about our sexual nature comes easy to some women and seems challenging to many others. We aren't taught much about sex unless we were lucky enough to have parents who weren't afraid to talk about it. Young people learn about sex from their peers or from experimentation. The older a person gets before she has experienced some kind of sexual encounter, the more ill-equipped that woman will feel when actually entering a sexual relationship.

When we feel well informed, practiced, and excited about sex it becomes an awesome experience. What we need is a sort of "owner's manual" – a guide to help us learn, give us ideas with which to experiment, and supply the guidelines to let us know that we are on the right track.

That's where this book comes in. Knowledge is key when it comes to being a Sex Goddess. First, you'll find out more about your body – as well as your partner's – than you ever thought possible. You'll also learn important communication skills that will enable you to feel completely comfortable during sex.

Then you'll be ready to explore the Kama Sutra and really turn up the heat. You'll learn how to give and receive pleasure in ways neither one of you ever imagined – and keep him wanting more.

before foreplay

*O*ne of the key ingredients to having a fulfilling sexual relationship is to make sure both partners feel valued and
appreciated. In today's go, go, go, world, it's easy to collapse
into bed every night, maybe have some maintenance sex, and
go to sleep. However, this is not conducive to building any
kind of relationship – never mind one involving heart pound-
ing sex!

So, this chapter is made up of ten easy gestures that you
can perform to remind your guy that there is no one you'd
rather be with than him. You'll both feel great after these – and
he'll be dying to show you just how much he appreciates the
effort.

GESTURE NUMBER 1: WAKING THE BEAR

The only items you'll need for this gesture are coffee, a coffee
maker, and the ability to get up a little early.

Before you hit the snooze button that second time, get
out of bed and make him his coffee. If you are a modern
woman – independent, strong-willed, and believe that you
were not born to be a servant girl – consider the cup of cof-

fee a gesture of love. More importantly, think of it as a means of keeping your sanity.

If he's like most men, he's a bear in the morning and *must* have that coffee before he will even acknowledge your presence. But if you greet him with his kill-the-bear juice when he stumbles out of bed, adjusting himself and muttering under his breath, he'll perk up instantly.

This is an ideal gesture for random mornings or mornings after he's had a particularly hard day at work.

GESTURE NUMBER 2:
DING-DONG. IT'S *NOT* AVON CALLING

Items you'll need for this gesture are a six-pack of his favorite beer, money for a pizza, and a little advanced planning.

Men love pizza, beer, and *Monday Night Football*. It's part of their genetic makeup. You can make Monday special for him by purchasing in advance a six-pack of his favorite beer and hiding it in a place he'll never look . . . where you keep the cleaning supplies, for instance. Put it in the refrigerator after he goes to work. Also, find out how much his favorite pizza costs and have a check ready for it. Plan to be absent for this gesture because your absence will make the gesture seem magical.

If he has a regular work schedule, phone in his pizza so it will arrive home just after he does. If his schedule varies, give him a call and find out when he'll be getting home. Don't worry. He won't get suspicious. He'll just think you're trying to keep tabs on him.

When he comes home, have the check and a note waiting under the remote control, which you've put in a conspicuous place. On the note, tell him you love him and want him to have the best Monday ever. Tell him to expect a knock at the door soon, which will be accompanied by a pizza. Inform him of the beer awaiting him in the fridge. It will be too early for *Monday Night Football,* but he can always heat up some pizza later. Come home after you're pretty sure he's gotten his pizza and is into his second or third beer. He will kiss your feet, and who knows what else. . . .

GESTURE NUMBER 3: ICE CREAM IN BED

You'll need all the makings for his favorite ice cream treat for this gesture, and you'll need to be able to put them all together first thing in the morning.

This is a twist on breakfast in bed, perhaps the oldest romantic gesture in, um, romancehood. There's no law that says breakfast has to have eggs, bacon, or even nutritional value. So, instead of hen fruit, break out the vanilla ice cream, hot fudge, whipped cream, and cherry. Make a towering sundae and wake him up with it one Sunday morning.

Make it more than just your average hot fudge sundae. Cover the ice cream with conversation hearts or little heart sprinkles, for instance. Serve him the treat on a tray covered with words of love written out of whipped cream. And if you're in the mood, you can find some other creative things to do with that whipped cream ... or with the cherry on top.

GESTURE NUMBER 4:
MAKING A GAME OF ROMANCE

For this gesture you'll need poster board, magic markers, a ruler, glue, scrapbook supplies, and your imagination.

It's not always easy for you to tell each other what you consider romantic or what you like in the bedroom, so why not make a game out of it – literally? This gesture takes a lot of preparation, but the rewards – for both of you – are worth it.

On the poster board, draw out game spaces. Be creative and use the scrapbook supplies – or pictures cut out of magazines – to fill in the spaces. Write down a list of questions to ask each other that correspond to the spaces on the board. You can use one set of questions or a "his" and "hers" set. It's up to you. Questions could be: What less-than-obvious part of your body is an erogenous zone? What would you like me to do to that part of your body? How do you like your kisses? Open-mouthed wide? Short or long? Tongued or sweet? Wild and fast?

This game gets you talking about intimacy and sex in a "nonthreatening" way. You know how embarrassing it can be to tell him you'd like more foreplay or that his kisses are too wet? Well, this game gives you the opportunity to get more out of intimacy and lovemaking. The best part is: He'll think you're doing this for him, but ... the benefit for you will probably be greater.

GESTURE NUMBER 5:
BABY, YOU CAN WASH MY CAR

You'll need super deluxe car wash solution, top-grade car wax, interior protectant, and some elbow grease for this gesture.

One weekend day, when he's engrossed in college or pro football – or taking an undeserved weekend nap – go out and detail his car. "Detailing" is basically the same thing as "washing," except that it's tons more expensive if you have it done professionally. First, wash the exterior of his car with the finest washing solution money can buy. For that, follow the recommendation of someone at the nearest auto supply store. Buy some of that special stuff that's supposed to be just for cleaning tires. Really make his ride sparkle. Pay close attention to the wheels, bumpers, and any other chrome-looking parts.

After you've washed his car from top to bottom, wax it. One way to make this easy is to buy an electric polisher/buffer. Buff his car until you could eat off of it. Then attack the inside. Vacuum it, then cover anything that's not glass or carpet with protectant. It cleans the interior and makes it shiny. Detailing also involves cleaning the parts of the interior that are overlooked – all the cracks and crevices, portions of the interior that are underneath the seats. If you don't want to go to that much trouble, it's okay. Just washing and waxing the car will be enough to make him spend the rest of the day detailing *you*.

GESTURE NUMBER 6: PLAYING HOOKY

All you need for this gesture is a sick day and the courage to claim it.

Relationship can sometimes suffer because both of you are so busy with what you think of as your "real life" – working forty or more hours a week. Even the best career path has stones and stumps strewn along it. If you've gotten to a point where you don't reach out to one another anymore, enduring those bumps in silence instead, then it's time play like a kid holding a thermometer up to a 100-watt bulb. It fooled mom into letting you take a day off from school. In a word: PLAY HOOKY, baby!

Play hooky together. Call in sick. Conjure up a couple of realistic-sounding coughs as you tell your respective bosses of the horrific maladies that have befallen you. Then get ready to spend the day together, doing what really you want to do: each other.

Focus on each other and bring out that little kid inside of you. Go to the park if it's a beautiful day. Play Frisbee. Have a picnic. Drink wine out of bottles in paper bags. Swing each other on the swings, and then go see a movie. Seeing a movie is the perfect activity for your clandestine day of fun and excitement. You don't have to worry about somebody from work seeing you out when you should be sick in bed, and you both will likely have the whole movie theater to yourself. Then, head home and go straight to bed – but no sleeping here.

GESTURE NUMBER 7: BUBBLES AWAY!

For this gesture, you need a clean bathtub, bubble bath, bath oil, candles, and music.

You love to soak in a hot bathtub filled with tension-releasing suds, right? Well, even though he would never admit it, he does too. You can make his day by having a bubble bath ready for him when he comes home from work or a day of golf with his buddies. Prepare the bath the same way you like it: aromatic candles everywhere, gentle music playing, tons of suds, and soothing bath oil. Most companies offer a variety of oils: to soothe aches, to increase energy, to put you to sleep, etc. Use bathtub finger paint to write a sexy message on the tub wall to add to this romantic gesture. After you've made him nice and relaxed and set his senses ringing with all the candles, suds, and bath oils, he'll probably want to you to add one more thing to the tub: you.

GESTURE NUMBER 8: NAUGHTY AND NICE

For this gesture, you'll need new lingerie and panties for every day of the week.

If your romance is new, you can wear a potato sack, and he'll think it's the sexiest outfit he's ever seen. You can be in a pair of his tighty-whities, and he'll be overcome with desire. As time passes, sex often becomes less exciting. And if you've been married for a while, it can become a chore akin to paying bills or a pleasant, though infrequent, diversion. If you want to bring lovemaking back to the forefront of your relationship, then appeal to the horny teenager that still lurks within him, buried under distracting adult responsibilities. Surprise him with new lingerie and panties for each day of the week.

Your local shopping mall probably has a couple of stores devoted to lingerie, and if it doesn't, most large department stores devote a major chunk of real estate to intimate apparel. If money is an object – and you or a good friend has seamstress talents – take items already in your closet and give them a new look. Sew naughty sayings into your sexiest pairs of panties. Add new lace and trim to an old bra for a new look. Make sure he notices your new "outfit." Tell him you'll have another surprise for him the next day. It's sure to spice up your romance – and may make you late for work a few mornings.

GESTURE NUMBER 9: SURPRISE DATE

For this gesture, you'll need a car, a bandana, some cash, and some planning.

Tell your man to dress casually for the night because you're going out, and you're going to surprise him at each destination. Go to the car, get out the bandana, and tell him to put it on – no peeking. Take him out to eat, to the last place he'd expect. After dinner, blindfold him and take him out for some old-fashioned fun: miniature golf, bowling, the skating rink, etc. Take him either to a place you know he'll like, or to a place you think he's never been. It's up to you.

End the evening by picking up his favorite dessert and taking him back home. Have him keep the blindfold on, so he won't know where you are. When you get to the driveway, hand him the dessert and see if he can guess by smell what it is. Then, tell him you're out at Lovers' Lane, and you're going to rock his world. If you're afraid neighbors will see what happens next, then take off the blindfold and say something like, "Would you settle for a night with a beautiful woman who loves you?" Then, take him inside and rock his world. Once in the bedroom, have him put the blindfold back on. Then tease and tantalize him with a variety of sensuous scents and tactile sensations. Let the remainder of the evening surprise you both.

GESTURE NUMBER 10: HIS FAVORITE MAGAZINES

For this gesture, you'll need to get a subscription to a so-called gentlemen's magazine.

Men are visually stimulated. And it doesn't matter how much he loves you. He'll notice other women, and impure thoughts will run through his one-track mind. Gain some control of that track by getting him a subscription to a men's magazine.

You may wonder, "Why would I want to give my guy magazines filled with pictures of beautiful, Amazon-breasted women whose headlights are always on and privates so sensuous?" Why? Because he'll love to get them and because it will show him that you are confident and comfortable enough with yourself to give them to him. Men love secure, confident women . . . and if he doesn't, then you're with the wrong guy.

Besides, providing him these visual stimulants will benefit you as well. They can only enhance your foreplay (hopefully) and lovemaking.

what is great sex?

*f*or some people, just being able to have any sex at all is considered "great." For others, great sex must transport the partners to a state of blissful oneness of body, mind, and spirit. For most people, great sex is any sex that brings a deep sense of satisfaction and fulfillment to both partners. What does great sex mean to you? This is an important question to consider. How can you possibly satisfy the needs of your lover – and have your own needs met – when you're not sure what you or he consider to be great sex?

WHY CAN'T SEX BE SIMPLE?

Why all the fussing and fretting about sex? Why can't sex be simple? Well, it could be, if the human mind didn't have the tendency to want to be in control of the human body. Most people have been taught to trust their minds and to ignore the messages from their bodies. All the major institutions of socialization – churches, schools, businesses, and even the family – teach you to control your impulses so you don't get into trouble or embarrass yourself or someone else. As you get older, the mind begins to exert yet another type of control.

You learn that it's not safe to do things that might offend or upset people. So you learn how to behave to get other peoples' approval. By the time you have your first adult sexual experience, the whole area of sexual relationships has gotten pretty complicated. You have learned numerous strategies for controlling yourself and for manipulating the opinions and feelings of others. This situation does not bode well for enjoying a lifetime of great sex.

Worry is one of the "common killers" of great sex. Humans worry about everything. Most of the time it is a futile exercise that keeps us from diving deeply into intimacy.

In spite of this early conditioning, the life force remains strong. It just needs to be encouraged, and it will bounce back. This book can help you get back into harmony with your own essential nature and reclaim your own life force. With a little patience and practice, your sex life can be transformed from something mundane or problematic to something wonderful and fun.

NOT JUST MAINTENANCE SEX

Great sex is not just any sex at all; it is certainly not what may be called "maintenance sex." Maintenance sex is what most people do most of the time when having sex – where partners perform sex more as a routine than as a conscious, intentional celebration of their love. Maintenance sex is entirely accept-able, but it is not to be confused with sex that is *really great*. Maintenance sex generally involves some degree of compro-mise – a step or two down from one's ideal. Perhaps only one partner is in the mood, and the other complies. One of the partners may be trying to appease the other. Or maybe, at times, one or both partners simply want to do the minimum to maintain their sense of being sexually connected.

Great sex will usually take more time than maintenance sex – the time spent staying in shape for it, the time spent preparing for it, and the time spent doing it – but all the extra effort is surely worth the results!

By contrast, great sex is usually transformative and heal-ing for the partners. Partners feel loved and cherished, and all seems right with the world. Great sex can help us transcend our separateness from one another. We both become part of something larger – a spiritual connection that puts us in touch with the oneness of all creation. Great sex may not happen automatically. But it can be learned. To have great sex requires knowledge, skill, patience, time – and practice!

And Much, Much More

After having great sex, people often report that petty ego concerns and personality conflicts seem unimportant. Competitive ideas about feminine and masculine roles or responsibilities tend to fade. The stresses of "looking good," being in control, feeling separate, or being "on guard" disappear. Great sex involves honesty, trust, letting go, merging, and just "being."

Great sex is not so much about technique as it is about presence. The most technically skilled lover is nothing without an open, trusting presence and attention to her partner. Learning new positions, techniques, and tricks is only a vehicle for experiencing each other's presence in new ways.

Think of great sex as a bonding experience. Sharing your vulnerability with your partner creates a special connection that can help you deal with the not-so-fun parts of the relationship.

Great sex is a type of intimate communication. It is one of the most important ways in which you, as a human being, share who you are with your partner. Really great sex is like melting or dissolving into the Divine, that universal state of oneness – with the lover and the universe – that gets you in touch with the sacredness of life.

WHAT IT REALLY TAKES

There are only a handful of key elements to having great sex: curiosity, openness of heart and mind, the willingness to try new things and learn, and a willing partner or partners. Within that handful, though, there is a vast array of possibilities for self-expression. The skills and techniques in this book are meant to enhance your own unique self-expression – this isn't a one-size-fits-all cookbook.

Sex as a Metaphor for Life

One could say that how you "do" sex is a metaphor for how you "do" life. Your sexual relationships reflect the same habitual patterns and survival strategies, learned as a child, that you exhibit in other areas of your life – except these patterns are often even more pronounced in the sexual arena. If you want to change one or more of the habitual ways you react to things, sex is a good place to start.

If you have trouble asking for what you want, for example, sex is a good learning laboratory. It's an area of life that is concrete. The feedback you get from your actions is clear: You either ask or you don't – and you either get what you asked for or you don't. With such clear and unequivocal feedback, learning is more likely to occur. And when you learn a basic life skill such as self-expression, this learning will easily transfer to the other areas of your life. It is the premise of this book that a life of consistently great sex is possible and that it can be fun to "train" yourself to get there.

Beyond Your Wildest Dreams

Learning new sexual and sensual techniques can bring you more than simple physical pleasure. You may also find yourself feeling a sense of ongoing unity with your lover. Healing can occur not only with respect to your sexuality, but also in your faith and trust in life, your emotions, and your health. Your overall self-confidence will grow as you learn to communicate and understand one another better.

Sexual healing has vast ramifications. Whenever you experience healing of past blocks or inhibitions, you tend to become happier, more generous, and more self-trusting. And you tend to pass this happiness on to those around you. When you feel loved, understood, sexually fulfilled, and connected, you become much more powerful as a human being. This is especially important for those women and men who were taught to suppress or deny their natural sexuality.

RELATING, NOT CONTROLLING

You cannot manipulate yourself into wanting great sex. And you certainly cannot manipulate someone else into wanting it with you! If you are willing to be open about what you do want, without attempting to control the outcome, then you may just get it. If you want to have great sex, don't have sex out of obligation, and don't ever force it upon your partner.

There is a principle governing intimate relationships that most people are just beginning to discover: When you try to make something happen the way your mind thinks it should happen, things rarely work out exactly as planned. The issue of "getting wet" is a good example. The more you think and plan, the less you are "in your body." You are in your head, or your mind. And when you are in your head, you're not very sexy.

Another way to say this is that in any given moment, you can *relate* to the person you are with or you can try to *control* that person. You can be a part of what is actually going on – feeling what you feel and sharing this energy with your partner. That's *relating*. Or you can try to make yourself or your partner feel something that you don't or maybe hide what you are feeling in the interest of creating a particular impression or achieving a particular outcome. That's *controlling*.

In sex, as in other forms of human communion, relating works. Controlling usually backfires. As you read this book, you will encounter numerous examples of how this principle works. The goal here is to help you enjoy great sex by learning to let down your guard, trust yourself, and, ultimately, trust life. Then, the need to control things that are not in your control anyway will fall away.

SOME BASIC PRINCIPLES ABOUT SEX

Sex is a vital aspect of life that can result in both new life and in a profound experience of oneness between partners. It holds the potential for allowing you to partake in the divine nature of creativity, which includes both procreation (birthing a child) and co-creation (birthing new ideas, products, services, or works of art). Sex can also be a great source of pleasure, joy, and fun!

Life operates on the principle of mutual benefit. A relationship, as a living system, is a good place to experience this principle. The more high-quality attention you put into your relationship, the more high-quality benefits you will derive.

The experiences of a lifetime are the curriculum that allows you to learn about your true nature and develop your

WHAT IS GREAT SEX?

innate gifts and talents. If life is a school, Sex and Intimate Relationships is the advanced course. If you welcome these lessons as opportunities to learn about yourself and to expand your capacity to deal creatively with life, then you will feel happy most of the time.

Honesty Is a Prerequisite for Intimacy

If you want to have an intimate relationship, not a superficial one, complete honesty is necessary. If you keep secrets from your partner, you are affirming that you cannot trust that this person has your best interests at heart. If you do not trust a person in this way, ask yourself, "Why would I want to have sex with this person?" If mistrust is present, it's a good idea to be honest about this. Often, honest communication reveals your own projections, baggage, or recurrent fears held over from childhood. Expressing them honestly can allow you get over them.

Your feelings of mistrust may reveal more about you than about your partner. This is one reason why it's good to share what you feel and think – so you can discover the hidden layers of truth about yourself that may underlie your feelings about your partner. Sometimes fears about telling the truth are based on false beliefs learned in childhood. Now that you are an adult, it's time to update your beliefs about what is really safe and what is really dangerous.

Risk-Taking Leads to Confidence

If you fear doing something that you really want to do, it is usually a good idea to go ahead and take the risk. You may want to pause and honestly assess the risk before doing so, but more often than not, the risk will turn out to be more about damage to your ego than to your essential being. Most interpersonal risks are not life threatening. Remember that fear is not a sign to turn back but rather a sign that you are moving into unknown territory. If you take the risk and survive, which you probably will even if it doesn't turn out as you'd hoped, your confidence will grow.

You Are Responsible

You are responsible for your own experience. Whatever you feel or think about another person is a mirror of where you are. If someone does something that upsets you, you are responsible for your feelings of being upset. Likewise, when you feel satisfied with something your partner did, you are responsible for that, too. The other person does not "make" you happy. Likewise, he does not "make" you upset.

Saying that you are responsible in no way implies that you are to blame or that it is your fault. Concepts like "blame" and "fault" are fabrications of the mind. They represent the mind's attempt to be in control by "understanding" what happened.

Your lover or partner is not responsible for your pleasure. You are. Learning about your own body – what you like, how you respond, and how to ask for what you want – are essential skills for great sex. Blaming your lover for not giving you orgasms or not doing it "right" will get you nowhere. Empower yourself to learn the skills to ask for what you want in a straightforward, loving, and truthful way.

Presence Is the Prize

The only time a relationship really works is when both people are in the here and now. This principle shows up most dramatically in sex and lovemaking. If your mind is on something else, you cannot make authentic contact. Presence is a prerequisite for great sex. And great sex is a pathway to greater presence. Practicing the exercises and suggestions in this book will give you the tools you need to be more present during lovemaking and in each and every moment of your life.

Pleasure Is Your Birthright

Our bodies are pleasure instruments that need to be played to stay in tune. Why would nature have given you erogenous zones if you weren't meant to do something with them? By learning to play that instrument, with all the skill you can develop, you train your body to receive great amounts of pleasure. When you know how to receive, your view of the world changes. You see the world as benevolent and trustworthy. Then you give that energy back to the people in your life.

Transforming some of your sexual experiences into sacred rituals will help your bodies to remember the event. This will cause you to look forward to more sexual and sensual experiences, which will then begin a feedback loop that becomes self-reinforcing. Life will look fresh and alive.

THE ADVENTURE BEFORE YOU

This book has been designed to be both a resource guide and an inspiration to you. It covers a vast array of information on anatomy, intimacy, relationships, latest discoveries, and fun sexual and sensual techniques. Good relationships and great sex go together, so you'll find both topics covered here.

You'll see how old attitudes from your past can block pleasure and honest self-expression. You'll have the opportunity for self-assessment so you can get an up-to-date view of yourself instead of operating from an outdated self-image. You will be guided to understand where you are now and to develop a plan for where you want to go. You'll have better tools to decide what you want out of life.

Sex is one of life's most wonderful gifts – whether, at any given moment, it is wonderful for you or not. It can be a great teacher. Although it can be fraught with anxiety and stress, it can be easy, fun, and relaxing. If you want to discover your highest potential for great sex, trust yourself and don't be afraid to try something new. If you do, one thing is for sure – your capacity for aliveness and pleasure will grow. At the very least, this book could lead to some of the cheapest and best dates you've ever had in your life. Use it well and enjoy.

loving your body

*a*ncient cultures, which held a positive view of sexuality, believed that your body is a temple, which you receive to care for in this life. If you don't take good care of it, who will? You are at your best when you are healthy, happy, and balanced. And, of course, having a healthy body leads to great sex! In fact, aerobic fitness has been found to be one of the factors that contribute positively to both a man and a woman's sexual experience.

BODY IMAGE IN OUR CULTURE

Today, even supermodels may complain about how imperfect their bodies are. If they can't accept their bodies, how can the rest of us accept ours? Women especially are bombarded with images of the perfect body. We're told to suck in our stomachs, wear high heels to appear taller and slimmer, and wear tight clothing. One of the reasons Western cultures have illnesses like anorexia is because we teach our young women that thin is the only way to be.

Self-consciousness and self-doubt get in the way of surrender to full sexual expression. They occupy your mind and keep you from focusing your attention on the physical sensations that bring you pleasure. Many lose themselves, agonizing over whether they're "good enough" or "pretty enough." Don't fall into this trap!

For some of you it will be a long process to unlearn the negative attitudes you inherited about bodily pleasure as children. You probably weren't encouraged to learn about your body and what brings you pleasure. When you "touched yourself," some bigger person would move your hand away from "down there."

Others received more painful negative reinforcement. You may carry guilt and shame regarding your sexual feelings, desires, and actions. Your body may carry the physical memories of those hurts just as your mind and emotions do. It's important to understand that the hurts and injustices you may have experienced in your early years can hold you back from being a fully expressed sexual and sensual being.

LEARN TO LOVE YOUR BODY

When women love their bodies, they naturally eat right, exercise, and stay healthy without worrying about the details. But getting to that place of acceptance and love so that you can nurture your body temple may be a challenge for you. Your family history, the stresses of modern life, and the perfectionist ideals you hold may stop you from full acceptance. Once you become aware of your unfriendly attitudes toward your body and understand how you learned them, you can begin the journey to greater self-love.

You can start to change your negative attitudes by learning to love your body right now. If you do, you won't have to look back forty years from now and say "Why didn't I just love myself the way I was?". Start now.

Don't ever let anyone be critical of your body. It's okay to ask for advice, but it's not appropriate for anyone to be critical of any part that is you. It is emotionally dangerous to have someone else dictate what is right and what is wrong with your own body.

Begin by noticing how often you worry about what your lover might be thinking of your physical features, whether it's your breasts, hips, or tummy. Notice how you talk trash to yourself. And start talking back. Tell yourself what you appreciate about your body. When you appreciate the gifts you have been given, the journey toward learning to love and honor your temple – just as it is – can begin.

Body Image Exercise

When you recognize that it is only you who hold yourself back, you can take back your power and discover your freedom. If you decide that as an adult you do not agree with some of the things you were taught as a child, you can make the decision to reclaim your vitality and your capacity for bodily pleasure. Here is a simple exercise that will be useful in all areas of your life:

1. Create an image in your mind of a situation or time in your life when you have felt really good about yourself. You feel empowered, smart, and capable.

2. Close your eyes and breathe deeply into your belly for a few minutes while you hold on to that feeling. Really feel it and breathe it in.

3. Now, imagine that you are feeling that way about your body: It is strong; it is healthy; and it is beautiful. Drink in that feeling and bathe yourself in it for a few minutes.

You'll find training for increasing the pleasure you feel in your many erogenous zones in an upcoming chapter, but for now, know that this little exercise, if you practice it, will vastly improve your sex life. Practice loving yourself!

TAKE CARE OF YOURSELF

When you view your body as a temple, you honor and hold it sacred. When you feel sacred and honored, you feel good about yourself. And when you feel good, you're more able to experience your fullest sexual pleasure.

Today we live in ever-increasing "busy-ness." The thing we all want more of is time. Women will often put themselves last on a list of the things that must be done in a day. There are the children and the dinner and the office and the laundry and so much more – the list goes on and on. But who's taking care of the caretaker? She must take care of herself, or she won't be able to care for anyone else. As the caretaker, you are relied upon, so you must take care of yourself.

Here's a hint about time: It all comes down to priorities. There is time for the things you really value when you schedule them in. You put meetings, project dates, social events, work, and your favorite TV show on your calendar, so why not schedule time for a long, sensual bath? Value yourself like you value these other things. Plan time for yourself, and put it on your schedule. Soon, it will get to be a habit.

Take a long bath. Put on music. Put a few drops of an essential oil in the tub. Pour in some bubble bath. Sprinkle in a few fresh rose petals from the garden. Any one of these things is so simple and yet will relax you and make you feel special.

Give yourself a pedicure. Do some gentle stretching or yoga. Give your feet a little attention. After all, they are your foundation. Find something for yourself that is a "treat" and make time for it. Everyone in your life will be happier that you did.

Try Another Body Image Exercise

Find an hour to yourself, a time when you'll have quiet and peace. Take a shower or a bath. Wash yourself lovingly and really feel your skin on your thighs, your chest, your buttocks, and your face. Let your fingertips move slowly and lightly over your skin. Your fingers should be enjoying the touch of your own body. Towel-dry and put on a soft robe.

Go into the room that has the largest mirror in your home and do the following:

1. Gaze softly into the reflection of your eyes for a few moments. (This may seem difficult, but don't be afraid to try it.)

2. Smile softly at yourself. Breathe deeply.

3. Separate the front of your robe and look at your body, slowly, with focus and attention. Notice all of the parts that you like. Why do you like each part? Has a lover said that he likes that part?

4. Take an inventory of the places and parts that you like and the reasons for liking them. Now, what parts are you not happy with? Why do you think this is so? What is it about those parts and places that you don't like? Can you identify whether these parts really don't satisfy you, or whether your judgment has been affected by cultural stereotypes of how you're "supposed" to look?

5. If you have any complaints about your body, say them out loud. Say them again, for as many times as it takes for you to understand that that is all they are – complaints. We start sounding a little ridiculous to ourselves when we repeat a complaint again and again. Do this now and do it up big time: complain, complain, and complain!

When you've finished, ask yourself how you feel. Often simply expressing a feeling can help it dissolve or change. Can you gaze upon your body with a little more acceptance and love? Spend just a final moment gazing in the mirror again. Relax, smile, and thank yourself for the new level of understanding you have.

THE CAPACITY FOR PLEASURE

The truth is that you have the same working parts that everyone else has, and that is all it takes for great sex. One culture will love big bottoms, another will love small breasts, and yet another will prefer hairless men. It doesn't matter what happens to be in vogue in your present time and place. You've got what you've got and your friend has what she has.

When you realize this, you'll be free to be in your body and experience what it is capable of. When you consider that it has been said that your brain is your biggest erogenous zone, you start to think about how little you might actually be feeling, and then you can begin using your body to its fullest pleasure capacity. When you get past focusing on your shortcomings, then you can begin to have access to your full pleasure.

EROTIC PRESENCE

Erotic presence, the way you radiate your erotic nature, is a key component that is missing for some people. This is not to say that you must become alluring, coy, and seductive, but rather that you become aware of your capacity for a natural eroticism. Grace, energy, and confidence allude to an erotic nature. Take the opportunity to notice what your style is and how you might develop it. If you go dancing, try upping the ante a little. Don't worry about technique; consciously throw yourself more fully into the steps and the swing. Be the dance. Let the energy flow through you.

If you feel self-conscious about erotic presence, try dancing at home just for yourself. Choose a time and place where you have privacy. You might want to dress in a sarong or something a bit sexy. Find a scarf or feathery boa you can wave around. Put on music with a good rhythm and start to move. You can dance in front of a mirror if you'd like.

Do a Body Wave

Stop censoring your movement – just let yourself go. Try a new move. Wave your arms around. Keep it light. Loosen your pelvis up with some body waves. To do these, stand with your feet a little apart and bend your knees. Relax. As you begin the movement, stick your bottom out and then gently swing your hips forward. When you feel comfortable with this, begin to let your upper body move to the wave. Your spine will become looser and the wave will move up to your neck and head. Do this slowly and as you repeat it, begin to smooth out the movements. Let your head go and include the natural action of your arms. Go with the flow.

This is an excellent way to warm up for lovemaking. You may even get to the place of being able to dance for your lover. Pretend you are a temple dancer. What better erotic foreplay could you imagine?

Add a little lingerie to your lovemaking. Try wearing a demi-bra or a push-up bra, especially when you're on top.

With a little practice, it will become easier for you to let yourself go. You'll begin to notice other areas in your life where you can apply this same idea. The big shift will be apparent in your lovemaking, but beyond that, a sense of erotic presence will energize your whole life. Find opportunities to be graceful and confident. Notice how you might add a bit of spice to that moment – especially if your partner is around to reap the benefits.

EROGENOUS ZONES

Your whole body is one big erogenous zone. Touch applied to your hair follicles and nerves on the skin travels to the brain and is translated to erotic, sensual feelings of pleasure. But some areas are more sensitive than others, so your body's erogenous zone can generally be divided into three types:

1. Primary (first-degree) erogenous zone: Mucous membrane tissues that comprise the lips, genitals, and nipples. These areas include the anus, vaginal lips, and inside the outer third of the vagina. They are rich in nerves and the nerve endings are very close to the surface of the skin. These areas are very responsive to touch.

2. Secondary (second-degree) erogenous zone: Parts that have a sparse amount of hair and are often found in the regions next to the third-degree areas. These parts are not as sensitive as the primary erogenous zone, but are more sensitive than the areas covered by hair.

3. Tertiary (third-degree) erogenous zone: The areas of the skin that are covered with hair – arms, legs, parts of the chest, and so forth. These areas have fewer and more dispersed nerve endings, so they are the least erogenous. Nevertheless, the hair follicles' ends, down under the skin, help stimulate the nerve endings that are buried near them.

Humans need touch from the time they are born to become healthy individuals. Our skin and nerves grow in their ability to feel more fully as we develop. This process can be expanded your whole life long. You will always have the ability to increase your capacity to feel the pleasure of touch.

A Key to Great Touch

A key ingredient to great touch is this rule: The hand that is giving the touch should feel just as good (or better) than the body part receiving the touch. In other words, the Giver should be in pleasure along with the Receiver. Think about this – it's quite a concept. The next time you give pleasurable touch to a person, think about your fingertips. Are they enjoying themselves? How could they be enjoying this experience even more?

When you start paying attention, you will find that you can really enjoy being the Giver. You'll find new ways to touch that will open up the experience for both of you. This simple practice will transform sensual touch for you *and* your partner.

It even works when the Giver and the Receiver is the same person. Try it in a fun way; be light and playful.

The Pleasure of Touch

Here is a fun exercise for increasing erotic, physical pleasure through touch. You can do this alone or with a partner as an experiential evening of erotic play. If you do it with a partner, it will involve direct sexual activity. If you are practicing solo, you can self-pleasure your genitals with one hand and stimulate other erogenous zones with the other hand.

The training idea behind this practice is to make new or deeper neural connections between the excitement you feel in your genital area and other areas of your body. For instance, let's take a basic example. Let's connect the pleasure you feel in your clitoris with your nipples. You or your partner would stimulate your clitoris to the point of arousal and then begin to simultaneously stimulate your nipples in whatever way you like. This could be orally or with either of you using your fingers and hands.

If you're doing this exercise with a partner, make sure you are lovingly communicating what works and what isn't working for you.

Next, continue the genital stimulation but switch to another erogenous zone. Connect each new area with the direct genital excitement you are feeling. Some areas will work better than others, but remember that every inch of your skin is covered in nerve endings that can learn to experience more pleasure.

Even the areas between your fingers and toes are exquisitely tender and sensitive when touched lightly and playfully.

More Erogenous Areas

Here are a few other erogenous areas you may concentrate on as you perform this exercise:

- Breasts and underarms
- Toes and feet
- Buttocks and anus
- Inner and outer thighs
- Neck area, ears, and face
- Love handles and sides of the torso
- Back of the knees and inside the elbows
- Fingers and wrists

By working on your secondary (second-degree) and tertiary (third-degree) erogenous zones, you are training your body to feel much more. After some practice, it is even conceivable to reach orgasm just by having your nipples sucked. As some of you might imagine, the possibilities are endless.

When the breath is connected to this practice, it too can be used as the vehicle to orgasm. Eventually, it may even be possible for you to breathe the way you did during this exercise and reach orgasm without physical contact. This is not far-fetched and is, in fact, a common practice in tantra. Can you imagine how beneficial this will be in helping you to achieve an orgasm *with* genital stimulation?

getting to know the male body

One step on your journey to becoming a Sex Goddess is to become familiar with the male form. Almost as equally important as becoming familiar with his body is being familiar with his heart and mind. Only when you are aware of all the elements of your lover's body and mind can you begin to satisfy all of his urges — in ways neither of you have ever experienced.

MALE SEXUALITY

It's a cultural stereotype that sexuality comes naturally to men. In fact, many men feel stymied by cultural and family beliefs that stigmatize male sexuality. In many cases, a young man's sexual experiences begin with quick, furtive exploration. He may learn to reach climax quickly during masturbation and then, when it comes to sexual excitement with a potential lover, his body may react too quickly. This pattern can be very difficult to change, leading to insecurity and fear of underperforming.

The male ego is very much tied to sexuality — issues of acceptance, performance, attractiveness, and youthfulness really do matter for men just as much as for women. When you add to this the stress levels of modern life, things can get tough. Lack of good communication skills between couples and the changing roles of men and women compound the problem. Often the last thing on the list is to take the time to develop skills as a great lover.

THE MALE BODY

The male body is very different from the female body in terms of its reproductive organs, but new advances in medical understanding of both the male and female anatomies is revealing more similarities than differences. Modern researchers are discovering that men and women have internal and external sexual parts that are of the same origin. As the embryo develops, these parts take different developmental tracks, as directed by male and female hormones, which exist in different ratios in the male and female bodies.

Pubic Mound and Pubic Bone

Men and women both have a soft, fat-padded pubic mound, which protects the pubic bone. It is covered with hair and has scent glands that distribute pheromones, sweat, and sexual stimulus scents.

The hair and hair follicles add extra erotic input by stimulating the nerve endings under the skin. Gently tugging, pulling, and scratching this area can be a turn-on.

The pubic bone protects the male's internal sexual parts from outside damage. In the right positions during sex, it can be effective in rubbing against the woman's clitoris for stimulation.

Scrotum

The scrotum is the sac that hangs down under the penis and contains the testes and the ductwork that allows the sperm to enter the penis and be ejaculated. The skin of the scrotum is soft, pliable, and covered sparsely with hair. Some men enjoy stimulation of the scrotum during sex.

Makeup of the Penis

The penis is comprised of several parts. On the exterior, the penile skin has an amazing capacity to expand and shrink within minutes or even seconds. As the tissue underneath fills with blood, the penis goes from flaccid to erect. Blood vessels can be seen just under the skin. These become much more prominent as the erection becomes harder.

At the tip of the penis is the foreskin. Just like the clitoral hood protects the clitoris, the foreskin covers and protects the delicate tip of the penis. If it has been removed via circumcision, the head of the penis is always exposed. The foreskin has many nerve endings and scent glands buried in it.

Many ancient cultures understood the sexual arts both as a science and as a spiritual path. The phallus was worshipped as a powerful creative force. These cultures bestowed names to the penis like Thunder Bolt, Wand, Jade Flute, and Arrow of Love.

The penile shaft has several nerves, veins, and arteries running through it and includes the urethra, which runs through the middle. The shaft is made up of the same spongy material as the clitoral shaft – the corpus cavernosum. When this spongy materials fills with blood, the penis becomes erect.

Up to one-third of the penile shaft is buried under the skin. At the other end, at the tip of the penis, is what's known as the Lowndes crown. It is buried under the tip, or head, of the penis and may be likened to the tip of the clitoris. It is highly likely that the nerve endings here are chiefly responsible for the exquisite sensitivity of the frenulum, the membrane that connects the foreskin to the shaft and glans, close to the tip of the penis.

The glans of the penis is the very sensitive tip area. It contains a large number of nerve endings and plays a key role in male arousal. The urethra, which connects the bladder to the penis, ends here and is used for the elimination of urine; it is also used during the ejaculation. Two spermatic ducts feed semen into the urethra during the ejaculation process.

At the base of the penile shaft are the two Cowper's, or bulbourethral, glands. They excrete small amounts of an alkaline fluid that neutralizes any acidity in the urine and urethral tube. This enables the sperm in the semen to travel in a favorable environment.

Prostatic Glands, or the Prostate

The prostate is actually a group of glands clustered together at the base of the penis. The duct that delivers the sperm and the two ducts that deliver the seminal fluid all convene here, so the prostate is instrumental in male ejaculation. During ejaculation, the prostate contracts and "pumps" the fluid out through the urethra.

The prostate is thought to be the equivalent of the G-spot in the woman. When directly stimulated, it is reported to add additional heightened sensuality to a man's orgasmic experience.

The Testes and Sperm

The testes are two egg-shaped glands that produce sperm. They are connected to the prostate gland, where the sperm are combined with the seminal fluids to form semen, which is then ejaculated through the vas deferens, or spermatic duct. The sperm contain the genetic material that the male contributes to fertilization. Although there are many sperm in each ejaculation, it takes just one to fertilize the egg during conception.

Prior to ejaculation, the sperm is held in seminal vesicles, sacs that hold and nourish it. The sperm bathe in a solution of simple sugar and fluids that thickens the blend until it is needed in the ejaculation process.

Perineum

The perineum is a soft spot on the exterior of the body, between the anus and the base of the penis. Although it's not always apparent that this is a sexual part, the many nerve endings that surround the anus make it very sensitive. Men can experience great pleasure when the perineum is pressed firmly, perhaps because it stimulates the prostate gland.

DOES SIZE REALLY MATTER?

Penis size is the subject of magazine articles, talk shows, kitchen table gossip, locker-room whispers, and you name it. As a result, many men feel self-conscious about their penis, afraid that they're just not measuring up. But the truth is, size doesn't matter – what matters is the man's self-confidence and skill.

The Lock and the Key

One reason the size of a man's penis isn't very important is that the G-spot is only 1½ to 2 inches inside the vagina, and during intercourse the goal is to stimulate the G-spot to an orgasm. The head of the penis does most of the stimulating of the G-spot. As the head passes the G-spot area, on both the in- and the outstroke, it catches slightly and that's what causes stimulation. Particularly on the outstroke, the head of the penis rubs up against the pubic bone and causes friction in the G-spot area.

Reassure your man that his member is more than sufficient for your needs. By building his confidence and encouraging him to feel confident and sexy, you're guaranteeing a better sexual experience for both of you.

sexual response in men and women

W hen you're hot, you're hot, and when you're not, you're not – and many factors determine how turned on you are at any given time: The quality of communication between partners, self-esteem, stress, feelings of warmth or closeness, family problems, stimulation or lack of stimulation, fatigue, aerobic fitness, and religious beliefs all affect your libido.

READY OR NOT

You can't expect to always be ready for sex. Yet many people would rather fake interest than communicate openly about their feelings. The problem with this is that it further increases the emotional distance between partners and makes great sex even less likely in the future. When you don't feel like talking much, you can simply say, "I'm not ready for lovemaking just now, but I sure would love to snuggle or spoon with you," or "I would love to give you a massage."

To get the most out of sex, it's good to understand some things about how men and women work. Let's look at the general sexual response patterns of men and women and then expand on the possibilities. A massage can help both men and women get into a loving mood. Some men feel they should be the macho, sexy guy who is just supposed to "get it up" anytime. The fact is, especially as men get older, they too need to be warmed up to enjoy sex to the fullest.

SEXUAL RESPONSE CURVE

Sexual response in men and women can vary greatly, despite the common belief that men are always ready for sex. In reality, men need touch, desire, and attention to feel turned on, just as much as women do.

Sexual Response in Men

Preconceived notions of male sexuality can actually hinder a man's full sexual response. Fortunately, ancient techniques have been rediscovered that can help him to achieve the fullest expression of his sexuality.

Men tend to be visual responders. They are stimulated by the sight of breasts, hourglass waistlines, and buttocks. When a man sees a woman walking down the street, his testosterone kicks in, and as his penis expands, his self-control shrinks. The typical male sexual response pattern unfolds like this:

1. Excitement phase: This phase begins with imagination, touching, innuendo, kissing, fondling, looking at the partner, flirting, dancing, or any other activity the man finds exciting. As excitement builds, his erection hardens. On an arousal scale of one to ten, this phase takes him to about five or six.

2. Plateau phase: An increase in excitation occurs. The heart begins to beat faster, the erection gets firmer, the sense of separateness fades to the background, and body movements become more involuntary. The testicles and scrotum tighten and pull closer to the body. Breathing patterns can be shallow and fast. His turn-on reaches a level of six to eight. Premature ejaculation sometimes occurs during this phase.

3. Orgasm phase: For men, the point of no return occurs as he begins to move toward orgasm and ejaculation. The penis thickens with blood and the head often swells as he gets closer to orgasm. The typical arousal level at the point of no return is at the eight to nine.

4. Resolution or refractory phase: Within minutes of ejaculation, the body relaxes, the breath deepens, and the blood begins to flow back out of the primary erogenous zones. The body comes back to its static state, before it was turned on, though much more relaxed and satisfied. Depending on the age of the man, the last phase may last for ten minutes or many hours.

An ancient Taoist love text says that a woman's sexual energy begins in her heart and then moves to her genitals. For the man, the energy starts in the genitals and then moves to the heart. This difference, when worked with consciously, can bring about the healing of misunderstandings between men and women.

Sexual Response in Women

It may be a myth that women take longer to warm up to the idea of sex than men do. For women who are very familiar with their bodies, not much time is needed for them. Many women reach orgasm quickly through self-stimulation but take longer to arouse and orgasm when having sex with a partner.

Regardless of individual arousal time, a woman's sexual response usually begins with feelings of emotional intimacy. You may not need such intimacy every time, but things generally go better if you feel you are getting the intimacy you need.

As a woman becomes sexually stimulated, her chest may flush, her vulva will begin to swell, and she'll start exuding lubrication in her vagina. Her nipples may become erect and her breasts firmer. Her heart rate and breath will speed up.

In the 1960s, sexologists Robert Masters and Virginia Johnson were the first modern doctors to research and describe in detail what we now call the female sexual response pattern.

The typical female sexual response pattern looks like this:

1. Excitement phase: The energy builds during this first stage of sexual excitement. Vaginal tissue swells, and lubrication of the membranes occurs. The supporting muscles of the pelvic floor tighten and pull upward. This expands the back of the vagina so it can accommodate the penis. On a scale of one to ten in terms of excitement, this phase may be rated at one through seven.

2. Plateau phase: The excitement response builds to a certain plateau and tends to level off. The turn-on becomes sustained and consistent at between seven and nine. Breathing patterns can be shallow and fast, and the erogenous zones change color to brighter pinks and reds. It is during this period that tantric breathing can play an important part in increasing and sustaining the sexual feelings being generated.

3. Orgasm phase: The recognition that orgasm will occur has a distinct beginning. Many women feel this moment coming only to experience it fading and then returning. That pattern may occur several times before the orgasm phase moves into its final release. Many women experience frustration at this juncture and find that the actual orgasm may be elusive If the orgasm does come, a very pleasurable explosive release of pulsating energy occurs. There may be multiple phases of pulsating explosion and release.

4. Resolution or refractory phase: The body relaxes, the breath deepens, and the blood begins to flow back out of the primary erogenous zones. The body comes back to its static state, before it was turned on, though much more relaxed and satisfied. For some women this phase will last for just a few moments; others will feel complete and won't want to be aroused again for some period of time.

When it comes to research of human sexual problems, men get most of the attention. In the United States, 95 percent of all funded sexual dysfunction research goes to find cures for male sexual problems.

EXPERIENCING MULTIPLE ORGASMS

Many men experience having multiple orgasms when they are in their twenties, and these almost always include ejaculation. As men enter their thirties, though, changes begin to occur. The refractory phase lasts longer in older men because it takes longer for the penis to refill with blood after a first orgasm with ejaculation. Men can learn to shorten this refractory phase, or they can try to achieve orgasm without ejaculation.

In women, multiple orgasms can be defined several ways. The orgasms can be back-to-back responses that have distinct beginnings and ends, or they can be so close that it doesn't feel like any refractory period has occurred.

During extended multiple orgasms experienced by a woman, constant waves of involuntary muscle contractions occur. As the vaginal walls contract, the vaginal fit usually gets tighter. Rather than diminishing the woman's sexual energy, multiple orgasms often get successively more intense.

A Variety of Ways

Back-to-back orgasms can occur through clitoral, G-spot, or vaginal stimulation. With women who typically have these orgasms, there is virtually no refractory or rest stage. They move almost immediately into repeated plateau stages and then orgasm.

Typically, if a woman were able to have several clitoral orgasms in a row, they would occur with a distinct beginning and end with a fairly short refractory phase. She would be ready to go again quickly and could take clitoral stimulation again, though she may have to start very softly the second time around.

In the case of G-spot or vaginal orgasms, they can occur like clitoral ones where the response cycle is repeated in its entirety, or the orgasms could be indistinguishable from one another. There would be no refractory period and the orgasmic state would simply continue – often being experienced as successively more intense rather than diminishing.

Take Yourself into a State of Bliss

Some women report sustaining a state of orgasmic bliss without dips for several hours. While this may be surprising, these are women who have learned to do this through practicing the exercises that are presented in this book. A woman can train herself to experience great amounts of pleasure. This is something any woman can do – with sufficient motivation and focused attention.

MASTERY OVER EJACULATION

Tantrics and Taoists practice ejaculation control techniques that are said to allow the *chi,* or life force energy, to build in a man as he ages. The teachers of these practices today say that a man may have orgasms but should retain his semen, to increase his energy and sexual drive. These techniques take some practice, but in most cases, if your partner is willing to learn them, he is almost guaranteed results.

It often takes just a few weeks to become very proficient. Your lover will last a lot longer and you will feel the benefits too. Within a month he should be able to actually feel the orgasmic sensations without ejaculation and the loss of fluid. He'll feel much more energized and sexually alive instead of depleted after sex. We will discuss orgasm mastery and control in Part Two of this book.

ENHANCING THE FEMALE ORGASM

There are several ways in which you can enhance your orgasm, whether they're clitoral, vaginal, or G-spot orgasms. Arguably, the easiest type of orgasm to achieve is the clitoral orgasm. As a woman becomes more stimulated and turned on, the shaft and crura of the clitoris become engorged with blood. As this happens, the shaft straightens out and becomes erect, much like a penis. In the process, the head of the clitoris actually becomes more buried under the clitoral hood. This can become a problem if the woman maintains a body pose that tightens and curls inward as she becomes more turned on. The clitoris tends to get further buried. Learn to relax your body and even arch your back, slightly, if you feel this might be the case.

Some women have learned to facilitate access to the clitoral tip by pulling back the clitoral hood. Usually this will happen after a woman is somewhat turned on already. As she needs more stimulation, she will help expose her clitoral tip, either during oral sex or with finger stimulation. The clock exercise is a very important exercise that is rarely taught. Try it by yourself or with a partner.

The Clock Exercise

Lie on your bed with your partner at your side. On your back, spread your legs open wide and relax. Take in a few deeply relaxing breaths. Now, as your partner watches, take your index finger, with a lot of lubrication on it, and feel your clitoris gently on all four sides. Now, notice if one area or side feels more excitable than another.

On most women, if you use the analogy of a clock, the 10:00 or 2:00 positions on their clitoris are by far the most sensitive. Most women don't know this. It's such a tiny area that most women think that the nerve bundle covers the whole thing. Not true. You will most likely be much more sensitive at one of these points than the other.

When you have found which part of the clitoris is most sensitive for you, have your partner touch you softly so that you can guide your partner to the exact spot. As you move into oral sex, make sure you are in a position that actually focuses on this area. After you have tried the exercise and explored the sensitive areas of your clitoris, take note when you are making love to determine if you are getting the most direct stimulation you can.

G-Spot Clues

Women can also achieve orgasm through stimulation of the G-spot. The more you explore the G-spot and focus on it as part of your sexual experience, the more alive and responsive it will become. At first, some women will experience burning sensations, the urge to urinate, mild pain, or possible numbness. Some women will feel like laughing or crying, or they'll feel waves of emotion. Some will experience sexual pleasure immediately. If you don't experience pleasure right away, take the view that you have at least taken a step on the path to ecstasy. If it feels like a struggle in the beginning, take breaks, but keep exploring. With time and patience, you'll get to the pleasure you're seeking.

Be gentle with yourself the first few times. Don't make it a chore. As you become more aware of your sensitive vaginal parts, you'll begin to notice how much you can feel during intercourse. The more you can feel, the more pleasure you'll have, and the more you will take control of your orgasmic response.

FEMALE EJACULATION

Until recently, many women have felt ashamed or embarrassed about exuding fluid during sex, but public opinion has changed. Now women tend to feel that the ability to ejaculate gives them a sense of erotic power or a sense of freedom. As more women talk to each other openly about sex, they have empowered themselves to feel good about whatever feels natural and pleasurable.

Ejaculating can be messy, and it is certainly not necessary for great sex, so it's important to know that it isn't strange or unusual. If you have experienced ejaculation, you might want to be prepared with a towel next to the bed. Some women have been known to ejaculate up to several teaspoons of fluid.

The fluid emitted is exactly like male ejaculate, only without the sperm. It is not urine, though because the ejaculate comes through the urethral tube, it may push out a small amount of urine prior to the release of the ejaculate. Considering that the fluid most often occurs through G-spot or vaginal stimulation, and that the G-spot is the urethral sponge or female prostate gland, this makes perfect sense.

As in the male, the fluid in the female prostatic gland builds up and needs release. Some believe that symptoms of PMS might be greatly alleviated by female ejaculation. Part of the pressure and fluid buildup during the menstrual period may very well be female ejaculate. If you have PMS and know the times of the month when you feel the symptoms the most, have a lot of sex just prior to these times – it may help.

SEXUAL DYSFUNCTION IN WOMEN

For women, overcoming and transforming problems with orgasmic potential can feel daunting at times. Learning to relax your body can help you learn to relax your mind. This will help take off some of the pressure.

Sit down and have a really good conversation about your beliefs, struggles, inhibitions, and frustrations with your husband, partner, or lover. Be vulnerable and tell your partner your innermost feelings. Lack of communication is the number one cause of libido problems, so stop beating yourself up and start expressing yourself more. For a little while, have sensual times together that aren't necessarily sexual or don't involve intercourse. You can focus on your partner for part of the time if you wish, but have at least two-thirds of the time together focused on you. Receiving a massage, snuggling together – these kinds of things can help take the worry out of being close.

Drop the focus on the big O for a while. Be sensual. Learn to relax and receive. If you are willing, have your partner blindfold you and give you a sensual massage. The blindfold will add a little suspense and newness and will allow you to focus on sensations more fully.

As you receive the massage, don't expect to end up having sex. Explore your erogenous zones fully. Be touched and learn not to do anything about it except moan. Let your lover know that in learning to receive, you are taking action, and, if he is patient, you will both see great results.

Educate yourself about your own body. Spend as much time as you can to learn what works best for you and what feels great. Experiment. Don't hold back. You have nothing to lose and everything to gain. You are in charge of your pleasure.

If you really feel stuck, visit a doctor of sexology or a psychologist with a sexuality background. You'll learn a lot and discover that you aren't alone. They will have a variety of ideas and, when combined with what you've learned in this chapter, will give you new tools for attaining your maximum pleasure potential.

enhancing both of your orgasms

*T*he big "O" – so exquisite, so sought after, so powerful, or so soon, so elusive, so disappointing – and we really know so little about it. We've had to discover the world of sex and orgasm on our own – each of us an intrepid explorer without much of a map. Bound by instinct, hormones, peer pressure, and the deep desire to please and be pleased, we seek to discover the "how to" of the great, soul-fulfilling orgasm.

WHY DO HUMANS EXPERIENCE ORGASMS?

The basic answer to the question of why humans have orgasms is procreation. To ensure that humans will continue to reproduce, nature has given us the orgasm as a sensual reward. Why would we have the drive to have sexual relations if there wasn't something very enjoyable about the act? After all, the clitoris has no biological function other than pleasure, and yet it has the highest concentration of nerve endings in the whole body.

While no two orgasms are ever alike, nor are we able to

describe each man's or woman's individual experience, we know the basic path the orgasm takes each time we are graced with the experience. The important part is that the orgasm depends on each person's capacity to feel and receive pleasure.

Scientists have discovered that when the female experiences an orgasm, the cervix actually dips down during each contraction and "sips" the semen up into the uterus. It's perfectly clear that throughout evolutionary history both men and women needed orgasmic pleasure to drive the survival of the species.

Pleasure Is Your Birthright

Nature has given us the sex organs, the hormones, and the desire to have sex. We have the capacity to fantasize, to think about sex, and to actualize the act through lovemaking. It is your birthright to have the fullest sexual pleasure you can possibly experience. You may choose to fully partake of your sexual potential, or you may choose to abstain. And, of course, you may choose anything in between.

You, and only you, are responsible for you how much pleasure you experience. Your partner is not the responsible one. If you hold ideas about the "shoulds" and "shouldn'ts" of sex that limit your capacity for pleasure, it's time to ferret them out. In a sense, the mind can be the greatest "sex organ" or the worst inhibitor of bodily pleasure.

If you're openly curious about your own sexual response cycle and give yourself permission to have pleasure, you will open up to new worlds. If you shut down your natural openness through false expectations and limiting beliefs, your capacity for pleasure diminishes. Taking charge of your sexual pleasure will empower you and free you in ways that extend beyond the bedroom.

LEARN TO ENJOY YOURSELF AGAIN

Men and women are supposed to be good at sex; yet we live in a culture that hides sexuality or confuses it with symbols of power or powerlessness. A society like ours does not educate its young adults in how to honor and love one's own body. With rare exceptions, every young person must either reinvent the wheel or overcome huge prejudices in order to learn about sexuality and sensuality.

Approximately 26 percent of all women report that they never experience orgasmic release; that number was even higher until the late 1960s. Inability to experience orgasm is a frustrating problem that directly affects our self-esteem and our relationships. Many men ejaculate before their partner is even warmed up! These things can frustrate people so much that they decide it isn't worth it.

Our own problems can look so big and scary sometimes, we don't realize that almost everyone else has similar struggles. Openings occur when we are willing to talk about our lives with others; when we become vulnerable with our friends and lovers; when we decide to empower ourselves to have more in our lives – more pleasure and more intimacy.

The Keys to Great Pleasure

Don't get stressed out by your quest to achieve the perfect orgasms. Trust that with love, practice, and playful innocence you can begin to have the kinds of sexual experiences that you always dreamed of. The following list summarizes the basic ingredients of expanding the capacity to orgasm (we'll look at each of them in more detail in this Chapter):

- Learn to relax. Take hot bathes at quiet times. Take time for yourself. Go away for the weekend to a spa all by yourself.
- Become an excellent breather.
- Stay conscious during sex – don't drift away.
- Learn to meditate – it will help you learn to focus your attention.
- Know your body and what you like.
- Make noise. Sound helps your partner know what you like, and it helps you let go into a deeper experience.

Notice that there isn't anything on this list that even hints at "techniques." While speed, timing, placement, and new techniques are wonderful, they won't help you focus and expand into the pleasure. Personal mastery over the domain of your mind and body will.

Staying Conscious and Aware

Eye gazing with your partner will put you in full awareness and bring you to the "present" with your lover. Leaving the lights on or lighting candles during sex with eyes open is the best way to be bonded with your partner. When we are fully available, open to being seen, our capacity for merging and orgasm goes way up. Once you get used to relating in this way, you won't want to go back to the dark.

Learn to Meditate

What does meditation have to do with great sex? It helps us learn to focus our attention. One of the main things that gets in the way of the orgasmic response in women is worrying. We can't get the kids, bills, phone calls, groceries, business, and so much more off of our minds. Meditation for as little as twenty minutes three times a week will give you a wonderful new tool to draw on for relaxation and focus.

Unlearning Old Habits

There are some women who have learned to orgasm by keeping their bodies straight and stiff. They tend to tense up instead of relaxing into the pleasure. This is how they have taught themselves to orgasm.

Discovering your G-spot and beginning to develop the capacity to have vaginal orgasms, in addition to clitoral ones, can have the outcome of opening you up. Remember to breathe deeply into your belly, be patient, and love yourself.

These women may have a difficult time learning to relax and open up their bodies to new positions and feelings. It can be very difficult for some of them to open their legs into wide positions. The vulnerability of exposing their genitals to be seen, touched, and honored can be a lot to handle. But if you bring a gentle will, a playful and loving heart, and a little patience to the practice, you can reap the benefits of expanding your orgasmic capabilities. Unlearning old habits is always hard but usually worth the work and focus.

MASTERY OF YOUR BREATH

Breathing is not a conscious activity for most humans. We expect to just know how to do it. Yet the key to greater health and vitality, experiences of expanded consciousness, and the full-body orgasm is mastery of the breath. Yogis place a great emphasis on learning to deepen and lengthen the breath. Becoming conscious of the breath and its patterns is the first step in the process of expanding orgasm.

We're a culture of chest breathers. Chest breathing causes adrenaline secretions that can lead to panic and fear. We're taught to suck our stomachs in and wear tight belts and clothing. This pushes our breath into our chests. We don't know how to belly-breathe.

You can't relax your genitals when you're holding in your stomach. The body becomes rigid. It's very difficult to tighten and hold your genitals when your stomach is full of breath. Try it. A relaxed body leads to a more relaxed attitude, which will lead to a more relaxed life. The way in which you breathe can make a vast difference in the quality of your orgasms and your life.

Breathing Issues among Women

Women who don't orgasm easily often hold their breath as they get more turned on. As they approach a kind of transition stage on the way to peak arousal, say a seven or eight on a scale of ten, they will often hold their breath, and then nothing happens. The result is that the energy must be build up again, only to have the same thing happen repeatedly. It becomes difficult to smoothly transition to the next level of sensations.

As arousal gets going in women, they will often begin to breathe a little faster. If they become aware of their breath, they can then begin to "drive" the experience by purposely doing faster, focused breathing to increase blood flow and arousal. It helps, exactly as meditation does, to focus the energy and move from a sense of separateness to one of being merged with the energy.

A BREATHING EXERCISE

This simple but profound practice should take about fifteen minutes. Wear loose clothing without a belt and allow at least an hour since your last meal. Lie comfortably on the floor on your back in a quiet place where you won't be disturbed. Rest a few minutes and then begin to notice your breath. How are you breathing? Through your mouth or your nose? Does your chest rise, or is the breath coming from your belly?

After you've briefly observed yourself, put your hands lightly on your abdomen and begin to breathe into your belly, focusing on the spot where your hands are positioned. Take long, slow breaths through your nose and visibly but gently force your belly to rise and fall with the breath. You may really have to focus on this. Don't breath into your chest. This will be difficult for some people and easier for others.

A survey by Carol Rinkleib Ellison in her book **Women's Sexualities** *found that 38 percent of 2,600 women studied had not once had an orgasm during intercourse.*

Practice sustaining this slow, steady breathing as you continue to observe the gentle rising of your abdomen. Take really deep breaths. Make them slow and deliberate. Stay relaxed. If you're having difficulties, don't get frustrated. If this exercise is easy, just keep going. Keep this up for ten minutes.

Take It with You

Try practicing breathing as much as possible to help it become easier and freer. Notice the times during your day that you might be breathing your old way. When we are frightened or upset, we become chest breathers. This creates a feedback loop of increased anxiety. In those moments, attempt to consciously change your breath right then and there. You will calm yourself and be able to function much more effectively.

If you find yourself holding your breath at any time, take a long, slow belly breath and clean out your lungs. Continue with the deep belly breathing. If you notice that you're holding your breath during lovemaking and at the time right before orgasm, relax, let go, and expand your abdomen with your breath. A deep belly breath can open the channels to allow the full-body orgasm. It will help you relax and at the same time build up a charge faster.

Practice with a Partner

You can try deep-breathing exercise with your partner in several variations – as you're in the spoon position or when you're facing each other as you lie down or sit in the yab-yum position.

The spoon position is when the two of you lie front to back, with the person in the back placing a hand over the front person's heart. If you choose to sit face to face, sit cross-legged as close as you can get or in the yab-yum position – when one person sits cross-legged and his partner sits astride his lap, with her legs wrapped around him. Face each other, eyes softly focused and open.

Gently begin to breathe together. It is usually best for the slightly faster breather to follow the slower breather. (Often, women are slower breathers than men.) Stay relaxed and avoid making a goal for your breathing. Breathe into your bellies. Continue for about five minutes. You can also try breathing alternately.

MAKING NOISE

Breath and sound go hand and hand. Deep, resonant, low-register notes can transform your orgasmic abilities. They open up the body cavity because the mouth is usually pretty wide open and the energy flow gets much more accentuated. Sound and breath can lead to multiple orgasms.

Making noise during sexual play is a turn-on and helps us know where our partner is in the sexual response cycle. The signs of arousal and stimulation, especially in women, are very hard to interpret even with sound added. When we open up our mouths to let sound out, we literally open up the body cavity and allow the energy and pleasure to be transported through us.

It's almost physically impossible to make deep sounds while in orgasm and hold your pelvic region tight at the same time. Moaning opens up the pelvic region and relaxes the genital area, greatly enhancing the full-body orgasms that follow.

Practice making sounds when you are making love or when you're by yourself, just for the fun of it. Deep breathe into your belly and open your mouth. Let your mouth be loose and relaxed. On the out breath, feel the sound come from your belly, not your throat. Make low, deep moaning sounds.

If making sounds is new for you, let your partner know that you'd like to try it. It can even feel a little silly at first, but being vulnerable will draw your partner closer, so go for it. Consciously bring sound to your lovemaking so you can really see how it works.

POSITIONS FOR INCREASING
ORGASMIC RESPONSE

Changing and varying positions can be very helpful in finding new ways to stimulate the G-spot in women. They are also valuable in helping men to last longer and achieve mastery over their ejaculations. In addition, trying alternative positions keeps the energy new between partners and invites open exploration.

Positions that enhance the connection between the G-spot and the penis in coitus are ones that place the angle of penetration such that the head of the penis is pointing to the top wall of the vagina. Positions in which the woman is on her back and has her legs up or on her partner's shoulders work well to achieve this angle.

When the woman is on top, she can help guide the penis in the right direction and to the right depth for maximum effect. Positions that directly affect the clitoris are the missionary and its close cousin the CAT. It's best to rub back and forth in these positions rather than just thrusting in and out. Thrusting, in general, pulls on the labia minora and the clitoral hood, but the stimulation is, at best, indirect.

KNOW WHAT PLEASURES YOU

Changing positions, learning correct breathing, and controlling ejaculation will certainly help you enhance your and your lover's orgasms. But one often-overlooked and yet obvious point that needs to be made is that in order to fully enjoy yourself, you need to know what pleasures you. Take as many opportunities as possible to learn about your hot spots. What gets you juicy or aroused? Do words turn you on? How about teasing or seduction? Erotic dances from your lover? Small gifts? Tenderness?

Explore your body and how it prefers to be touched. Do you prefer soft caresses or to be squeezed and hugged? Do you prefer to be touched all over, or do you have specific areas that most desire touch? Do you like a single stimulation point, or can you handle two, three, or more? Do you like your nipples squeezed or your whole breast fondled with just a hint of nipple?

A person's preferences usually change from moment to moment. We'll like one thing this time and something else the next. But most of us find that we also have our favorite spots and secret desires when it comes to touch. The problem is, we keep them secret. Let your lover know what you like; but first, discover it for yourself. You won't be able to tell what you don't know. Our genitals are most sensitive to touch, but there are other erogenous areas you may want to explore:

- Breasts and nipples
- Inner arms and armpits
- Toes and feet
- Buttocks
- Scrotum
- Inner and outer thighs
- Anus
- Neck areas
- Down your sides from under the arms to the hips
- Love handles
- Back of the knees and inside the elbows
- Fingers and wrists

Try combining one or two of these areas with genital stimulation. Vary the touch by using fingertips, tickling, blowing, lightly scratching, or just holding the area. Learning to receive touch will create more possibilities for orgasmic pleasure.

CHAPTER 7

exploring the kama sutra

*T*he classic Eastern love manual, the Kama Sutra, is perhaps the most sought after reference to sexuality of all times. Translated and brought to the West in the 1800s, it supplied a set of guidelines that helped everyone in ancient India come to a similar understanding of their erotic nature. In modern times, the Kama Sutra began its most popular era in the 1960s, during the so-called sexual revolution. Today, it remains more popular than ever.

THE PARTS OF THE KAMA SUTRA

The Kama Sutra is a manual on conducting relationships between lovers. Best known by Westerners for its variety of exotic sexual positions, the Kama Sutra has as much to offer modern couples as it did their counterparts in ancient India. Though some of it isn't pertinent to contemporary lovers, here is an overview of how the original sutras were written and divided.

- **General Remarks**: The beginning (Part I) addresses the three aims in life: the obtainment of wealth (Artha), the rules and morals of behavior (Dharma), and the erotic practices to assure pleasure and the existence of life itself (Kama). It also addresses the learning and the acquisition of knowledge, conduct, and intermediaries for the lover.

- **Amorous Advances**: This section (Part 2) is the one that most of us know as the sexually detailed area. It describes positions, embraces, biting, oral sex, caressing, scratching, stimulation, desire, the behavior of women, and conducting a lovemaking session.

- **Courtship and Marriage**: This part (Part 3) details courting rituals and includes topics such as relaxing the woman, ways of convincing the woman to agree to courtship, and the forms of marriage.

- **Duties and Privileges of the Wife**: This area (Part 4) addresses both the situation of only one wife in the household and many wives within the residence. It details how the wives should conduct their lives, and offers psychological suggestions for the harem's peace and happiness.

- **Other Men's Wives**: This part (Part 5) examines the conduct for having an affair with another man's wife. The use of an intermediary is discussed, along with how to set up an encounter.

- **About Courtesans**: This is an extensive section (Part 6) dedicated to the courtesans. The section outlines ways in which they should conduct their lives and business affairs. It details whom they should take as a customer, what they should do in the acts of love, and how to manage long-term lovers.

- **Occult Practices**: Aphrodisiacs, spells, and potions are covered here (Part 7), as well as remedies for impotency and low libido. Plants, herbs, spices, and other products of the time are also mentioned.

A UNIVERSE OF EROTICISM

Due to a renaissance of interest in sexuality, personal growth, and spiritual seeking, the Kama Sutra is gaining new acceptance as it grows older. Western cultures don't have anything to rival the Kama Sutra. The erotically positive cultures of the past understood that sexuality was part of a healthy lifestyle. Pleasure, sensuality, and sexuality add happiness, fulfillment, and even more years to our lives.

"Kama" means pleasure or sensual desire. It is the name of the Indian God that represents the sexual nature in man. "Sutra" means short books or aphorisms.

The Kama Sutra supplied a set of guidelines that helped everyone in ancient India come to a similar understanding of their erotic nature. The need for this deeper understanding in the West fuels our attraction to this great treatise on the nature of human intimacy. The Kama Sutra is much more than a manual of positions, though this is an important component of it. The detail that is brought forth in the world's greatest love manual is done so with the attention of the scientist. The observations on men's and women's erotic and emotional nature are forthright and deep.

The variety of information in the Kama Sutra ranges from detailed kissing techniques to seduction and courting suggestions. It explores the idea of biting your lover to leave your mark on him or her. The instructions on scratching techniques are for the same purpose and to heighten the sensual feel of the skin during lovemaking. Thrusting techniques are mentioned. Some of the positions are named after animals, for this was one way to study man's relationship with the natural world.

Eros, the ancient Greek God of Love, is equivalent to Kama, the Hindu God of Love. Psyche, the Greek for Soul, is the Greek counterpart to Shakti, the supreme Hindu Goddess.

The Kama Sutra also describes techniques to stimulate the senses, including the ten types of "blows" and the sighs that accompany them. It details the way in which a man might grasp his *lingam* (penis) and churn it from side to side in the *yoni* (vagina) of his lover. It outlines the areas in the *yoni* to stimulate. You'll get the sense that the Kama Sutra was indeed considered a science.

THE FOUR AIMS OF LIFE

The Kama Sutra is part of an overall, complete picture of life that the ancient Hindus understood. Extensive writings, in the form of other sutras, were available on many subjects and were part of the well-bred citizen's life. Included in this were good health practices, the attainment of knowledge, an understanding of the universe and its workings, and the ritual honoring of the gods and goddesses.

> *On the acquisition of obtaining Dharma, Artha, and Kama: Man, the period of whose life is one hundred years, should practice Dharma, Artha and Kama at different times and in such a manner that they may harmonize together and not clash in any way. He should acquire learning in his childhood, in his youth and middle age he should attend to Artha and Kama, and in his old age he should perform Dharma, and thus seek to gain Moksha, i.e. release from further transmigration. Or, on account of the uncertainty of life, he may practice them at times when they are appropriate to be practiced. But one thing is to be noted, he should lead the life of a religious student until he finishes his education.*

The citizen held most important the first three of four aims in life; *Artha* – the accumulation of wealth; *Kama* – the knowledge and advancement of pleasure; and *Dharma* – the practice of worship and of having high moral standards. The fourth – *Moksha* – was the attainment of enlightenment and liberation from the cycle of death and rebirth. Being excellent at the first three assured the fourth.

Artha

The attainment of *Artha* meant that it was a citizen's moral duty to be comfortable in life and be able to support a family. The acquisition of material goods and the pursuit of economic interests was one of the main objects of life and included arts, land, gold, cattle, wealth, equipment, and friends. This was particularly true for the merchant classes and the traders. It was believed that you couldn't pursue the other two well if you were worrying about being able to feed your family or offer money contributions to the local temples.

Kama

To attain *Kama* one had to pursue the desire for erotic pleasure. *Kama* is the enjoyment of appropriate objects by the five senses of hearing, feeling, seeing, tasting, and smelling, assisted by the mind together with the soul. The sutras held the belief that sexual pleasure was one of the most enjoyable things man could do. It is the foundation from which we all came and was to be revered and sought after. Being sexually knowledgeable was a high duty not only for pro-creation, but for bliss and pleasure.

It was not to be indulged in to the point of ignoring the other aims in life, though. Many scholars believed that without *Kama* a person would not have the drive to pursue *Artha* or *Dharma*. This can certainly be seen when a married couple is about to have a child. The nesting instinct to provide for the family and child takes over and that drive is what causes the pursuit of the other aims in life.

Dharma

Dharma means "right conduct" and includes virtue, right-eousness, and truth. It is thought to be the most important of the three aims of life that lead to the fourth, *Moksha*. If there is ever a conflict of the three aims in life, then *Dharma* is said to be the one to follow. Cosmic and natural laws were seen as the highest paths of knowledge. Faith, devotion, and kind deeds were the actions to support the *Dharma* path.

Moksha

A basic tenet of Hinduism is the cycle of birth, death, and rebirth according to Karmic actions during a lifetime. *Moksha* is the liberation from this perpetual wheel, sooner rather than later. During a lifetime, if the person lives up to the three aims of life and sets a very fine example for themselves, they will shorten the cycle of Karmic action and move faster to the place of final resting – *Nirvana*.

ANCIENT SAGES AND MODERN SCHOLARS

The written form of the Kama Sutra came from a long his-tory of rich oral tradition. Writing had disappeared in India about 3,500 years ago with the advent of the Aryan invasions. Around 600 to 700 B.C. the ancient manuscripts were again written down in the Sanskrit language. Though the original "rules of love" were attributed to Nandi, the god Shiva's com-panion, it was a man named Babhravya who compiled the vast manuscripts of earlier days into a more manageable work some time between the seventh and eighth centuries B.C.

There were 1,000 chapters in the original work by Babhravya, called the Kama Shastra.

Vatsyayana

A scholar named Vatsyayana is attributed with the Sanskrit version that we know today. He wrote this condensed version from the original Kama Shastra around the fourth century A.D. The Kama Sutra was meant as a guide to be memorized and to have the more subtle points shown through interpretation of a lover or guide. Therefore, its structure appears as poetry and verse. The descriptions of the positions, morals, and guidelines are short and to the point. It's almost like they were meant as reminders to the couple, rather than as detailed instruction. In that way they can be remembered, until they become habit, during the early years of sexual relations.

Sir Richard Burton

The Kama Sutra is perhaps the best known of all the love manuals. It came to modern society when an Englishman named Sir Richard Burton translated it from Sanskrit in the middle 1800s. Burton was an intrepid adventurer and is credited with helping to discover Lake Victoria and the head of the Nile River. It is also believed he spoke forty languages fluently.

The Kama Sutra shocked Victorian England, and after Sir Richard's death, his wife burned many of the other books he had translated. Most of them have not been retranslated and indeed many may be lost forever.

The sexual mores in Victorian England during his life were very restrictive. Because Sir Burton traveled extensively, he may have experienced some of what is contained in the Kama Sutra firsthand. Other scholars of the subject understand that he was generous with his interpretations rather than staying within a strict translation.

Contemporary Scholars

In the last century there have been several important people in Western society who have helped reintroduce the erotic arts of the East into mainstream Western cultures. Alain Danielou, Nik Douglas, and Penny Slinger, among others, have been instrumental in translating to us the intricacies and subtleties of the ancient practices. They have molded the teachings, in the tradition of true teachers, to modern tastes.

Alain Danielou, renowned musician, racecar driver, singer, sportsman, traveler, and scholar, was born in Paris in 1907. He lived in India for many years. He studied the vina, a classical Indian string instrument, and became adept at Sanskrit and the Hindu culture.

In 1963, Alain Danielou returned to Europe with the intent of bringing Indian and Asian culture to the West. Since that time, he has written more than twenty books on Indian culture. Two of his more recent books deal with the profound effect the Westernization has had on the rich Indian culture. He sees the loss of the divine and the connection with nature that the Hindu culture has suffered at the hands of becoming "modern."

Nik Douglas and Penny Slinger created the book *Sexual Secrets* in the early 1970s. It is still the contemporary "bible" to the Kama Sutra and Tantra, a mystical path that employs sexuality as a vehicle to enlightenment. Through Nik Douglas' scholarly words and Penny Slinger's incredible artwork, the Western World were introduced to the Kama Sutra and began to grasp the concepts put forth. Their active participation and deep understanding has opened up these insights for modern men and women.

THE OTHER KAMA SUTRAS OF THE WORLD

After A.D. 400, a series of "books" or aphorisms appeared in several Eastern cultures. They were manuals on lovemaking. They included guides for couples on kissing, touching, positions in lovemaking, attitudes, moral obligations, and much more.

The Perfumed Garden

The Perfumed Garden was written in Arabia in the sixteenth century. It has a treatise on the many different sizes and shapes of penises and vaginas (*lingam* and *yoni* in Sanskrit). Accordingly, it details thirty-five types of *lingams* and thirty-eight types of *yonis*. Written primarily for men, it counsels them to ask the woman for instruction on giving her pleasure. It also contains teaching stories of various sorts and many intercourse positions.

The Ananga Ranga

The Ananga Ranga was written in the sixteenth century in India. It details morals, seduction techniques, sexual positions, hygiene, rituals and sexual spells, aphrodisiacs, and other erotic concepts. It pays particular attention to the woman learning to control her pelvic floor muscles to heighten the experience between her lover and herself.

The Secrets of the Jade Bed Chamber

This treatise on sexuality and sensuality includes recipes for potency remedies, exotic positions, and counseling on the ways of love. As with many societies that included eroticism in their cultural heritage, there is symbolism in the words selected for use in the books and by lovers. A Jade Stalk meant a man's *lingam*, whereas a Jade Garden refers to the woman's *yoni*.

Metaphors to the ways of love are used extensively in Eastern cultures; some are amusing while others are erotic and secretive.

The Ishimpo

The *Ishimpo* was a manual that originated in Japan as the erotic teaching manual for that culture. Similar to its counterparts in India and other parts of Asia, it depicted the sex act between man and woman as the essential force that controlled the universe. It expressed the importance of making love as the force in nature that keeps the earth circling the heavens.

Pillow Books

China, Japan, and most Eastern cultures had what are termed "pillow books" in addition to the teaching manuals mentioned above. These books were used by couples as erotic stimulants and as reminders of a human's vast sexual potential. They could be used when a couple got into a rut in their sexual and sensual relating. Pillow books were adorned with beautiful erotic pictures, poetry, writings, and suggestions that couples could consider together to stir their passions.

THE ROLE OF THE TEACHER

The sutras – whether the Artha, Dharma, or Kama Sutras – were written as aphorisms or short sayings so that they could be both memorized and taught and interpreted by a qualified teacher. The author's interpretation, or alternatively one by a scholarly associate, always accompanies contemporary versions of the translations. The language that the sutras are written in is often difficult for the layperson to understand, and the added help of additional teachings and commentary further the meaning of the information contained therein.

While the young lovers and students of the past enjoyed the opportunity to have a teacher to work with on the finer points of the Kama Sutra, people today may not always have that chance. As you read this book, help your lover and have him or her help you understand the subtler points. Act as each other's teacher so that you may both enjoy the delicious fruits of the love chamber. Guide and gently hold your lover in the arms of the gods and goddesses, and the centuries of lovers before you who have traveled the path of Kama, the God of Love.

CHAPTER 8

the kama sutra for modern lovers

Without a manual of our own, we have turned to the East to educate us on the ways of love. We're interested in the exotic, erotic maneuvers that the Kama Sutra brings us. Western societies have never developed a science around sensuality and sexuality, but it's recognized that there is a need for it. What better place to look than the Kama Sutra?

WHY ARE WE INTERESTED?

Our sexual nature is an important part of life, yet it has often been relegated to behind-the-door furtive acts that leave us frustrated, unfulfilled, and wanting more. As a society, we fantasize about cultures of the past and romanticize their relationship to love and the erotic arts. But we lack support in learning the arts of making love, and need a culture that encourages the sexual acts as a form of art. New generations see the Kama Sutra as the literary work that holds this promise.

Western Curiosity of World Cultures

The world is getting smaller and smaller through better communication and efficient methods of transportation. The influences of many cultures are beginning to blend borders between countries, and our knowledge is increasing about things that weren't available to us before.

The Kama Sutra was never meant to encourage promiscuity or sexual indulgence. Just as a little liquor adds a pleasant euphoria but too much leads to intoxication, knowledge of the sexual acts and arts enhances the act but doesn't give license to debauchery.

Sex sells things in Western cultures, but the fact that we actually *have* sex has been kept underground until very recently in our history. We're only just now coming out of our Victorian-like mindset about our sensual natures and our innate sexuality. We need a manual that provides us with the basic lessons by which to guide our explorations into the pleasure and bliss of sexual intimacy.

The 1960s Opened Doors

In the middle to late 1960s, the so-called sexual revolution opened the doors for many people to explore their sexual nature more fully. Indian culture was beginning to come to the West in the form of yoga, Ravi Shankar's music, madras shirts, incense, and Indian-imported clothing. The Beatles were meeting with gurus in India, and the Kama Sutra was being put into modern book form for the first time. The ways of the

East showed a new path to an area of life that the West had pushed under the covers, literally.

New Sources and Interpretations

The Kama Sutra was designed in short aphorisms so that couples could remember them and teachers could assist students in learning their finer points. The same is true today. Every book, instructional film, or love manual on the Kama Sutra places the author in the role of the teacher.

The Kama Sutras are a rich combination of the original words, and the knowledge that we have today of the body, the workings of the mind, and the understanding of psychology. Included in that body of knowledge is the relatively newfound freedom that Western women, as well as men, have gained in recent years.

INDIA THEN AND TODAY

Today's modern India is a product of Western thought and institutionalism, and is very similar to the United States and most of Europe. Though India primarily follows the Hindu faith, and not Christianity, it aspires to being – and is rapidly becoming – very Westernized. It prides itself on this fact and continues to move further away from its heritage of a sublime mix of science, spirit, and sexual freedom.

Women in India's History

India was, for most of its history, very progressive toward women, sexuality, the arts, and culture. Women had a lot of power and responsibility in the time of the Kama Sutra, as men relied on them for their opinions and thoughts on a variety of both everyday problems and worldly affairs. Most wives were, however, confined to the home compound, and women could not appear in public places unless an older woman or a male relative accompanied them. Whereas most courtesans could study the arts of love, as well as the many arts that were listed in the Sixty-Four Arts, including the sciences, commerce, languages, and music, married women had to seek permission from their husbands before engaging in worldly affairs.

The Sanskrit word Madana *means "love" or "sexual love." The word* Madanalaya *means "the female sexual organ."*

Modern India

Today's India has a large middle-class population that aspires to Western-style living conditions. Women work outside the home in all professions and manage to raise the children too. The computer sciences have taken India by storm and have produced numerous companies and brilliant individuals who have played a great role in the rapid advancement of technology in both the East and the West. The travel industry is booming in India, as well. Tourists from all over the world are drawn to this country by its interesting history, culture, and to Eastern teachers and gurus. India has much to teach the West, yet the Kama Sutra and sexuality is what brings many to its doors.

TIMES HAVE CHANGED

As revered as the Kama Sutra is today, many of its parts just don't fit modern society. Most civilizations around the world – both Western and Eastern – don't consider it appropriate to have more than one wife, but that was not true in the days of the Kama Sutra. In fact, much of the work includes details on how to handle multiple wives, and even lovers and courtesans.

Outdated Concepts

There are many things in the Kama Sutra that no longer fit both our modern sensibilities and our cultural beliefs. Though women did have a strong presence in some aspects of their lives in India, the equality of the sexes was nothing like we know today. And even though sexism still exists, even today, the line dividing equal opportunity between the sexes is thinning. From jobs to orgasms, women are claiming their territory with passion.

Portions of the Kama Sutra put the man's needs first and tend to have a male "voice." This makes sense since a man wrote it. Some of the sections, like the one on scratching, seem to imply that rather severe scratching and biting serve to "mark" the woman. The idea that she is "taken" by a very passionate man comes to mind.

The Issue of Polygamy

Kings often had many wives, but wealthy civil servants, traders, and merchants might also take more than one wife if they could afford it. The Kama Sutra describes, in detail, both the responsibilities of the wives and the man of the household. In another part, it even goes as far as to say that a wife neglected or beaten by her husband has every right to find another lover – and is actually encouraged to do so. Here are some interesting passages from the part of the Kama Sutra that describes such issues:

- At festivals, singing parties, and exhibitions all the wives of the king should be treated with respect and served with drinks.

- The women of the harem should not be allowed to go out alone, nor should any women outside the harem be allowed to enter except those whose character is well known. And, the work of the king's wives should not be too fatiguing.

- A man marrying many wives should act fairly toward them all. He should neither disregard nor pass over their faults, and should not reveal to one wife the love, passion, bodily blemishes, and confidential reproaches of the other. No opportunity should be given to any one of them of speaking to him about their rivals, and if one of them should begin to speak ill of another, he should chide her and tell her that she has exactly the same blemishes in her character.

- He should learn to please all of his wives in different ways. One of them he should please by secret confidence, another by secret respect, and another by secret flattery, and he should please them all by going to gardens, by amusements, by presents, by honoring their relations, by telling them secrets, and lastly by loving unions.

- A young wife who is of a good temper and who conducts herself according to the Dharma Shastras wins her husband's attachment, and obtains superiority over her rivals.

THE PRESENCE OF COURTESANS

Courtesans were revered and an honored part of society in ancient India, indeed in many cultures around the world, both Western and Eastern. Their company was sought out and they were the only women that could actually be seen in public at gatherings and community events. They were highly educated both in current events, languages, the arts and sciences, but especially in the art of love.

The Fine Details of Being a Courtesan

The Kama Sutra contains exhaustive details for courtesans. It describes the methods by which a courtesan should make money, what lovers they should take, and even how to get themselves out of debt and problems. "According to Vatsyayana, the principle reasons for becoming a courtesan are: Material gain, escape from physical or financial dangers, and the love for a particular person."

In Sanskrit, Garika *means "a courtesan who is pious, liberal, and devoted." A* Kumbhadasi, *on the other hand, means "a courtesan whose aim is the acquisition of wealth, physical comfort, and an easy life."*

The Kama Sutra also describes who should become a courtesan and what qualities she should possess. In addition, Kama Sutra recommends that the wives should – with permission from their husbands – learn the arts of love (and as many of the other arts as possible) in the event that their husband dies and they then must support themselves. Here's a list of qualities a courtesan was expected to have:

The qualities desirable in a courtesan herself are: Beauty, youth, marks on her body proving her good fortune, sweet speech, appreciation of virtues and accomplishments of the young man, not undue fondness of material gain, desire for love and physical union, consistency of mind, honesty and frankness in her dealings, ambition for acquiring extraordinary accomplishments, generosity, and appreciation of the Arts and of social gatherings. But the most common qualities which courtesans actually possess are: Intelligence, character, good behavior, honesty, gratitude, foresightedness, absence of inconsistencies, awareness of the properties of time and place, refined way of life, and expert knowledge of the science of love and its ancillary arts. They possess the absence of begging, loud laughter, speaking ill of others, citing faults of others, anger, covetousness, disrespect of the

*things that are to be respected, fickle mindedness, and inter-
rupting other's speech.*

A Courtesan's Value

Courtesans imparted a feeling of confidence in the men that courted them. They seemed to have an honored place in the best of society. They employed the help of friends and even their mothers to find good clients and trustworthy confidants. Very often one courtesan would have only a few lovers in her lifetime and be very close to them. But, the sages said, that if she wanted to be wealthy, she had to have many lovers of the highest quality. "The following list shows the value of payment in order of preference: Gold, silver, copper, bronze, iron, bedstead, blankets, silk cloth, perfume or sandalwood, chilies, furniture, ghee, oil, corn, and cattle."

SPIRITUALISM

The spiritual aspects of the Kama Sutra are threaded throughout the text and refer to the many aspects of love and the regenerative powers of sex. The Kama Sutra is born from the trinity of the three aims in life: wealth, pleasure, and good karma. As mentioned in Chapter 7, these lead to an afterlife that shortens the cycles of death and rebirth, and allows the citizen to reach heaven in a more direct path.

The Hindu Creation Myth and Kama

According to the Hindu mythological creation story, nymphs called *apsarases* served Kama, the god of love. They carried his emblems, or symbols, which were the fish, the conch shell, and the lotus flower – all elements that come from an association with water. Water is considered life giving, and it is a symbol of creativity and our sexual nature. These are all aspects of the second chakra – the sexual chakra. The lotus is also a deep symbol associated with the *yoni*, or the vagina. It is a regenerative symbol of life.

An ancient and most famous Tantric mantra goes thus: "The Jewel is indeed within the Lotus." The inference is that the Jewel is the seed, or semen, and that the Lotus is the *yoni*. According to the above-mentioned mythological creation story, the world and all of the gods were created and born from the Lotus, the womb of the mother.

Universal Symbols of Fertility

Shells have been associated with marriage and fertility from early times. The Greek goddess Aphrodite came from a shell and rose out of the ocean foam. Spring is the season of *Kama*. The fertility and fecundity of this time of year cannot be denied. Many pagan religions had ceremonies that were centered on fertility rites during spring. It is also said that it is in the springtime of your life that you are most interested in *Kama*.

CHAPTER 9

pleasure-enhancing practices

Though not strictly from the Kama Sutra, the more subtle arts of intimacy were part of daily routine in ancient India. These took the form of yoga, meditation, and rituals to honor the gods and goddesses. In this chapter, you'll learn about some of the pleasure enhancing things you can do to increase the quality of your intimacy and orgasmic capacity.

BEYOND THE KAMA SUTRA

The Kama Sutra is great for explaining exotic positions, details of the physical and emotional types of men and women that exist, and how to make a good match for oneself. It covers how to make money as a courtesan, how a good wife should act and the things she should know, and how to handle the harem. However, it doesn't cover the fine details that Western sexologists, psychologists, and educators have discovered in more recent years.

The Fine Details

The Kama Sutra does not go into the exact sexual techniques that pertain to the teachings for modern society. Details on how to pleasure a woman's *yoni* are not extensive. It does say that the woman should be satisfied but doesn't say exactly *how*.

It's difficult to know the more subtle parts of the treatise as the translations, especially Sir Richard Burton's, can be somewhat inaccurate depending on the bias of the interpreter. Some of the other holy writings that occurred in the Hindu culture of the time covered more of the inner realm or subtle properties that one can bring to intimacy and sexuality, such as yoga, meditation, an understanding of breath, and healthful living strategies.

Modern scientists, sexologists, and educators know that these fine details are very important to the experience of great sex. You'll find hints and tips throughout this book that give you much more detail than the original Kama Sutra. Remember, that was the prerogative of the teacher of the Kama Sutra — to add the fine details.

BREATH

Breath is the essence of life. It is something our bodies do without us thinking about it. If you ever take a beginning meditation class, the instructor will definitely point out the importance of the breath.

Types of Breathing

Many people have not been instructed in the proper way to breathe, which can be life enhancing. We are taught to suck in our tummies and wear tight clothing, including belts and corsets. This forces us to breathe shallowly into our chests rather than into our bellies. The results are that we never get a full, luxurious breath of air.

On the other end of the spectrum, belly breathing is grounding and stabilizing. Conversely, high-chest breathing is the type that is normally associated with the "fight or flight" phenomenon when we are frightened or anxious. This kind of breathing perpetuates itself because it causes hormones, such as adrenaline, to seep into our systems and cause anxiety. Relearning how to breathe is one of the most important things you can do to enhance your sexual experience and your life.

Researchers know that the way you breathe has a tremendous impact on your life. Fast chest breathing induces panic and distress while slow, deep belly breathing creates bonding, emotional stability, and longer life. They have also identified a few men and women who can simply breathe their way to orgasm.

Deep belly breathing will expand your capacity to have more powerful orgasms. When you breathe deeply and relax, it isn't possible to tighten the pelvic muscles. This leads to a more orgasmic response capability.

THE BASICS OF DEEP BREATHING

Deep breathing fills the abdomen first and then fills the chest cavity. The capacity of the lungs becomes larger when you fill the lower area of the lungs first and then the upper area. As a result, the breath will begin to slow down because there is more oxygen in the lungs to extend the breath. These are the basic steps:

1. Lie down on any firm surface – the floor or your bed if it's fairly firm. After you learn the techniques it doesn't matter where you are, but for now make it a firm surface.

2. Remove any restrictive clothing, such as tight waistbands or belts.

3. Close your eyes for a moment and breathe. Notice how you breathe. Where is your breath, in your chest or in your belly?

4. Place one hand on your stomach, below your navel.

5. Begin to breathe into the hand that is on your belly. Push it up on the *in* breath and let it fall on the *out* breath. Exaggerate this movement.

6. Slow it down and let the hand rise and fall.

Perform at least ten of these breaths the first time and then work up to thirty. For best results, try to remember to do this practice twenty times a day. Bring deep breathing into your consciousness as many times a day as you can. Come back to the breath like you would during meditation.

Feeling More Sexual Energy

Eventually you will breathe this way all the time, though it will take you some time to get to that place. Put little "Post-it" notes up on your car's steering wheel, on your computer screen, at the kitchen sink, by your bed, and any other place that might be easy to notice them. It's especially great to put reminders at locations where you may most get triggered to move into anxiousness, anger, or frustration. These are the places you will need calming breath the most.

Deep breathing opens up the body cavity to more feeling. It allows the orgasmic pulses and pleasure to move through the body instead of being locally focused in the immediate genital area. The direct results are longer, more powerful orgasms, more pleasure, and much less tension.

A Quickening Breath Specifically for Women

Women do tend to take longer than men to reach the orgasmic plateau stage during sexual intimacy. It's helpful to know a few tricks to get oneself aroused quicker and stay in that zone for longer periods of time. Building your sexual charge higher is an art that is well worth striving for.

Women who know how to raise their sexual turn-on more quickly have a greater capacity for learning and expanding even further. Try the following exercise by yourself the first few times. It's an exercise in breathing and visualizing so, again, choose a quiet place with privacy.

1. Lie on the floor or bed on your back.

2. Close your eyes and deep breathe into your belly for a few big breaths.

3. Now begin to quicken your breath. Breathe through your mouth but keep the breath in your belly, not the chest.

4. Do ten or twelve breaths like that, then go back to a few deep breaths.

5. Repeat the fast breaths, but at the end of the twelve (or so) breaths purse your lips and slowly force the air out through your lips. Visualize your breath, bathing the front of your body, with your mind.

6. Now locate your clitoris or your G-spot in your mind. You can pump your PC (pubococcygeus) muscles a couple of time to locate one of them. Focus on it with your mind and feel it with your mind. You are not touching yourself at all.

7. Repeat the rapid breaths and try to visualize your clitoris or G-spot as you do them. You can even pump your PC muscles.

8. Repeat a series of ten breaths, three times. Relax when you are done for five minutes, breathing deeply but at a normal pace.

How did this feel? Did you start to hyperventilate at any time? If you did, then slow down and take several deep breaths between the sets of fast ones. Did you feel aroused at any time? The next time you practice this exercise notice your arousal levels. Start playing with this edge to increase your orgasmic capacity.

The recommendation of exhaling slowly, through pursed lips, might come in handy for extending the period of time you feel your orgasm. This is true for both men and women. Try this some time.

RELAXATION

Most of us in the modern world lead very stressful lives and have hardly any time to relax.

We rush to school or work, then back home. We cook, clean, spend time with our families, get some exercise, pay the bills, and start all over again the next day. But knowing how to relax is the key to a healthy life – and a good sex life.

Relaxation means a complete shutdown of the systems that keep us alert and on the go. Silence, privacy, soft music, a deep massage, a soft place to lie down, eye gazing with your partner as you lie close together on the bed – all these are deeply relaxing. You need relaxation to keep you emotionally stable and happy.

The Relaxation Exercise

Try this easy exercise. Lie down on the floor in a comfortable position. Place your hands to your sides and take a few deep breaths. Now tense your whole body for just a second or two. Let it go – and this time really let go. You can try a big sigh with your out breath to help. Tense again and then let go.

Do you notice the difference? You may have thought that you were relaxed when you started, but when you contrast it to tensing your muscles and then letting go, you can feel the difference. Once you find this deep state of relaxation, fall into it deeper for five or ten minutes. Close your mind and let the world go for just a little while. Your body and psyche will love you for it.

EYE-GAZING

Eye-gazing is something you may not be used to. In this culture, it's often difficult to meet someone else's eyes. You avoid each other's eyes because you feel that you have to protect yourself. Sometimes, being vulnerable with any person you have just met isn't safe.

Be Seen

You can get out of practice at meeting another's eyes. This can even extend to your partners and lovers if you feel as though there is something you can't say to them. Being open and vulnerable with your lover means the lights have to be on – or at least a candle is lit. You must "be seen" and be able to "see" your partner.

When eye-gazing, you should not try to do anything. Just relax. You won't need a smile on your face or a frown or a quizzical look. Just think about being open and soft and receptive.

The Eye-Gazing Exercise

Sit facing your partner cross-legged or in two straight-backed chairs that are very close together. Your knees should be touching either way with your hands resting easy in your lap. Take a few deep breaths with your eyes closed to get relaxed. Open your eyes slowly and look into the eyes across from you. Nothing to do – nowhere to go – just gaze softly.

You may find that you want to giggle at first, or talk, or say that this is silly. Resist the temptation to giggle. Gaze into the eyes in front of you and see them as deep pools. Keep your eyes focused on your partner's for at least five minutes.

How did that feel? Did you find yourself dropping into your lover's eyes even deeper? Try eye-gazing up-close next time, say, five inches from his face. How does that feel?

What's in It for You?

Eye-gazing opens your soul to another. You have a chance to drop your defenses and practice being vulnerable. When you are physically close to someone you love the chemicals of love get transmitted more readily.

The brain chemical category of endorphins produces comfortable attachment to family and partners; oxytocin produces bonding and physical intimacy; and dopamine, PEA, and norepinephrine cause us to feel excited and "high" on attraction and expectancy.

Pheromones, the attraction chemicals your body produces, are transmitted via your breath. Oxytocin, the bonding chemical produced during lovemaking, orgasm, and childbirth, builds up when you gaze lovingly with your mate. Oxytocin improves your immune system, calms your breathing, and

lowers your blood pressure. Those are all valuable compo-
nents for a healthy lifestyle and they're produced by love and
connection.

BUILDING SEXUAL ENERGY

This technique is designed to heighten the sexual energy
between you and your partner, as well as to expand your personal capacity for increased pleasure. Like most of us, you were
probably taught to dummy-down your capacity for extended
pleasure. Re-learning how to receive pleasure, build upon it,
and spread the sensual and sexual energy you are being given
takes practice.

Spread and Receive Sexual Energy

In this exercise, each partner will take about a twenty-
minute turn and then switch until both partners have had a turn.
You can actually continue this erotic exercise for as many turns
as you'd like. It's also an exquisite way to start your lovemaking
any time you feel in the mood to tease and be playful. As a
woman, you should be the first to receive in this exercise.

*Ask yourself what is your uppermost capacity for receiving love
and pleasure? With the practices in this book, you'll begin to
transform the amount of pleasure you can receive. As a result,
you'll expand the pleasure you give to others, too.*

Arouse your lover sexually for three to four minutes in
whatever manner the two of you choose. Encourage deep

breathing and relaxation. Then, using both of your hands gently spread the energy up the body, away from the genitals, with four or five light strokes of the hand.

Instruct the receiver to take the energy you are sweeping over him into his upper body, along the spine and chest. Then, start the whole experience over again and continue until you have gone through four waves of building and spreading. You can now switch partners and repeat the exercise.

Use this technique during foreplay to arouse and tease your lover. It will enable the two of you to learn automatically how to expand the sexual feelings throughout your body every time you have sex. This will open the gateway to expanding your capacity to receive more pleasure. As can be imagined, this practice can be done solo too.

the art of erotic touch

*T*here is no better way to express love than through the art of touch. Touch is a human need and the art of sensual touching is a skill to be developed. The Kama Sutra describes many variations on the quality of erotic touch, the type of caress appropriate to the moment, and the passionate qualities associated with certain types of touch. It is a science unto itself.

SHOWING LOVE THROUGH TOUCH

The Kama Sutra offers very explicit and detailed information about passionate embraces, kissing, scratching, biting, shrieks and cries, and even striking blows (in certain ways and in certain areas of the body). While most amorous people will use these methods during lovemaking, some of the techniques are beyond what modern lovers feel are appropriate for them. With the additions of massage, conscious touching techniques, and knowledge of the body's erogenous areas, you will have the tools to develop your own erotic touch style.

Knowing Your Body

An understanding of your body, as well as your lover's, is immensely helpful when touching. Tender areas need to be loved in ways that don't cause your partner to react unfavorably by flinching or creating other disagreeable responses. Knowing your own erotic trigger areas and even developing new ones will add to your sensual experience. Once you know more about yourself you can begin to expand that knowledge to its greatest potential.

Some people are good receivers and some are better at giving. It is a rare and fortunate person who is good at both. Cultivating both qualities will give you greater pleasure in your relationship.

There are three areas of nerve distribution on the body and each corresponds to an amount of body hair and its distribution patterns. Basically, the more hair over an area of the body the fewer nerve endings per square inch that area will have. That does not mean, though, that those areas with fewer nerve endings are going to be less responsive to touch. It just means that they will respond differently. The areas are:

- **Tertiary**: These are the areas that have the more dense amounts of hair, such as the pubic triangle, the armpits, and the head.
- **Secondary**: These areas comprise most of the body and are covered with light, sparse hair. The secondary areas include the arms, the legs, the neck, the back of

the hands, the back and chest areas, the buttocks, and the inside of the thighs.

- **Primary**: This category is the genitals, the anus, the erect part of the nipples, the mouth, and any area where hair is absent.

Everyone is aware of the feelings generated in the genitals to erotic touch, but you may not think about your arms or legs as being sensual. Though the hair is generally thick on the pubic triangle — and thus has relatively few nerve endings — it is one of the more erotic places. By gently pulling and teasing this hair during sex, you can highly eroticize the pubic area.

Sensual and sexual massage is a healthy pastime. The body is filled with lymph nodes, blood vessels, muscles, and vital organs that need stimulation to stay healthy. Massage is an erotic pastime that will always be received lovingly from your partner.

Most people love when their head is massaged and rubbed. It is erotically pleasing to have your hair pulled, scratched, and scrunched by a lover. The nerve endings in the scalp and the pubic area are near enough to the buried hair follicles in the region to transfer the stimulated feelings.

The same is true for scratching, biting, and even firm sucking. You would probably love to have your back, head, or arms scratched during sex but probably not your vaginal lips. This would most likely hurt and not be appropriate because of the extra amount of nerve endings in this area. Love bites, sucking, and scratching should be placed in suitable regions on the body.

Training Your Mind and Body

Each and every one of the above-mentioned areas of the body is erotic to the touch, especially if you have trained your mind to feel it. A wonderful feedback loop can be created through conscious practice to connect any area of the body to sensational feeling. By stimulating the genitals in the ways you like best and stimulating another area of your choice, you can create both mind and body excitement to this new area.

Like a yogi, who can slow his breathing down to practically nothing, the body can be trained with practice and time to recognize a vast variety of stimuli and touch. It is in this way that you can truly give and receive the highest pleasure possible through touch. The first step is to bring your conscious mind to the task with your willing body.

It is known that some women can orgasm through nipple or other body part stimulation alone, without genital touching. These women have trained themselves to feel sexual in distinct areas of their bodies. There are also women who can have orgasms by simply breathing a certain way. They have trained their bodies to respond in ways that the scientific world is just beginning to understand.

Other Forms of Touch

Touching doesn't necessarily mean just touching with hands and physical body parts. You might consider that a sensual gaze or an erotic stare might be a type of touch. It touches your soul. Loving words, erotic speaking, eye-gazing, flirting with the eyes alone, dancing erotically for your partner – all of these things can be "touching." Sitting opposite each other and breathing in different ways while focusing on each other's eyes is a soul touch that can be very erotic to the practiced couple. Try dancing sometime to erotic music, such as belly dance or Middle Eastern music, keeping your eyes connected the whole time. Sway, seduce, and tease your partner while dancing. See how it "touches" you.

It is reported that the clitoris has approximately 8,000 nerves, all ending at its tip. That's twice as many as the penis has and many more than any other area of the body. It's no wonder the genitals are so sensitive to touch.

EROGENOUS AREAS OF THE BODY

Much has been written and discussed about erogenous zones. These areas of the body seem to be more highly erotic and sensitive than others. The amount of nerve endings in certain areas tends to distinguish parts of the body that are more easily used to help arouse an individual. Getting to know your areas and then developing a few new ones is great fun and can be very easily incorporated into love-play.

It is obvious that the genitals are the first regions to come to mind when you think of erogenous zones. In most people, when even slightly touched, the genitals react immediately with warmth, then a change of color, and then swelling. No other body parts act like that with such little coaxing.

Not much conscious attention is put to the other areas of eroticism in the body, though. You may forget to try stimulating some of the other areas during lovemaking, but in doing so you ignore some potentially powerful additives to the sensual experience. Here are some areas you may or may not have thought about before:

- Breasts, under the breasts, nipples, and underarms
- Toes, in between the toes, and feet
- Buttocks, anus, and perineum
- Inner and outer thighs
- Neck areas, ears, and face
- Eyelids
- Love handles and sides of the torso from the underarms to the hips
- Backs of the knees and inside the elbows
- Fingers, in between the fingers, and wrists
- The back and the head

THE KEY TO GREAT TOUCH

Following this deceptively simple rule will give you the key to great touch: The hand that is giving the touch should feel just as good (or better) than the body part receiving the touch. In other words, the Giver should be in pleasure along with the Receiver. Think about this — it's quite a concept. The next time you give pleasurable touch to a person, think about your fingertips. Are they enjoying themselves? How could they be enjoying this experience even more?

As the Giver, you will find that you can really enjoy this role. You'll find new ways to touch that will open up the experience for both of you. This simple practice will transform sensual touch for you. It even works when the Giver and the Receiver is the same person. Try it. Above all, this is fun, so be light and playful.

The key to fabulous touch is to remember that the fingers of the Giver should feel just as good or better than the body parts of the Receiver. This ensures that both of you are having a great time.

As the Receiver, you should concentrate on the touch you are receiving. Breathe into the quality of the touch to such a degree that your Giver can actually feel you receiving. Don't be afraid to make yummy sounds as a form of communication too.

The Blindfold Game

This is a great way to practice giving and receiving wonderful touch. You can improve your ability to give and receive each time you play and have a lot of fun, too. Take turns playing each role, possibly on different nights so that each of you really gets to honor and participate fully in the role you take. Set this game up as a ritual that will last for an evening.

Prepare the bedchamber with soft lights, candles, some incense, drinks, and anything else that you may need to be comfortable. You'll also need a blindfold of some sort. Gather a piece of velvet, a few rose petals, a soft makeup brush, a fringed scarf, a piece of fur, chocolate sauce, ice cubes, and anything else you can think of that might produce a sensual, erotic, but different kind of a feel. You may want to have some good-quality massage oil on hand, too, for a massage at the end of your exploration game.

You should encourage your partner to breathe deeply and relax. Encourage him to give you feedback and to make sounds of pleasure that he or she is feeling. Encourage and delight all the senses you can possibly bring into this love session.

Decide who will go first, then blindfold the person receiving and lie him or her down. As you treat the "receiver" to the sensual experience, see if he or she can tell what you are using. Try the different modalities on different parts of the body, seeing which areas are more sensitive than others. Remember the varying dynamics of the erogenous zones and use this knowledge to its fullest potential.

The Sensual Bath

The sensual bath is another way to honor touch as an art form and to practice giving quality touch. You can either take the bath together or separately, but remember that the point is to give and receive the best touch possible. Create the sensual setting by using candles, music, scents, and even rose petals in the bath water.

Wash your lover's feet lovingly. Massage his shoulders while they recline. Give him sips of fruit juice or wine. Present him with a warmed towel upon emerging from the bath. Gently towel dry him, and anoint him with a light oil or lotion when he is dry. Brush his hair thoroughly and sensually. Tell him that you love him and repeat it often. Now, switch places – it's your turn.

The Bath in Ancient India

The bath was an important part of the day's ritual during the time of the Kama Sutra. Great attention was given to the skin, teeth, hair, and general body. The hands and feet of women were often perfumed and painted with henna designs. Men shaved and shampooed every second or third day, but bathed (or dipped into water) everyday. They also used limited amounts of perfumes. The Kama Sutra makes reference to cleansing the armpits and oiling the body every other day, as well.

Every inch of your skin is erogenous. Your skin has many thousands of nerve endings so let your imagination run wild. Be respectful of your partner and his likes or dislikes. Remember to ask permission to touch an area you think might be risky or extra sensitive for him.

107

Women, especially in the harems, bathed together. Along with handmaidens, they helped each other bathe, shampoo, brush and braid their hair, dress, paint henna, and embellish their bodies. It was a time of social interaction too. Water has always held an important part in the culture of India. It is revered and thought to be holy.

EMBRACING

Many Westerners don't stop to think too much about the kinds of embracing they do, let alone give them names. However, this is the kind of thing you see in the Kama Sutra, and it contributes to the impression that sexuality comes down to a science for that culture. The names seem old-fashioned, but the actions are entirely recognizable today. Here are the four types of embraces detailed in the Kama Sutra:

1. Touching
2. Rubbing
3. Piercing
4. Pressing

Touching Embrace

"When a man under some pretext or other goes in front or alongside of a woman and touches her body with his own, it is called the Touching Embrace." When two people don't know each other (or don't know each other well) but seem enthralled by each other, they may create a situation so that they can touch. You've probably done it or at least thought about it at some point in your life. The titillation of just touching the person probably sent a rush of adrenaline through your body and made you long for more.

Very young boys and girls do this kind of thing to test the other person. It looks like teasing at a young age or even rough-housing, but it is that first spark of sexual interest rearing its head. When young adults do it, they are getting practice at just being in the presence of another person.

Piercing Embrace

When a woman in a lonely place bends down, as if to pick up something, and pierces, as it were, a man sitting or standing, with her breasts, and the man, in turn, may grab her and hold her, it is called a Piercing Embrace. This embrace seems very bold on the part of the young man. It is a teasing kind of maneuver that has the girl wanting the kind of attention that she gets. The above two kinds of embrace take place only between persons who do not, as yet, speak freely with each other.

Rubbing Embrace

When two lovers are walking slowly together, either in the dark, or in a place of public resort, or in a lonely place, and rub their bodies against each other, it is called a Rubbing Embrace. Getting as close as possible is always good. With this embrace, you can pass pheromones through your breath and convey sexual innuendos in your body language.

Pressing Embrace
When on the above occasion one of them presses the other's body forcibly against a wall or pillar, it is called a Pressing Embrace. By pressing or pinning, the couple is creating a private space where they can get closer and have their bodies rubbing more intentionally on each other.

At the time of the meeting the four following kinds of embrace can be used: The Twining of a Creeper, the Climbing a Tree, the Mixture of Sesame Seed with Rice, and the Milk and Water Embrace. If a couple had an attraction to each other and was possibly already betrothed, these four different kinds of embraces were used along with the Pressing Embrace to show the degree of sexual turn-on the couple had for each other. Each gets hotter than the other before it.

This is the kind of information the Indian society of the day taught to the young people so that they could be straightforward in their selection of a life partner. They were not beating-around-the-bush when training young lovers.

SCRATCHING AND MARKING
Scratching during sexual arousal and intercourse occurs when the partners are very turned on and passionate. It is very

common for the passions to run high, and scratching your lover can help increase the passion. The Kama Sutra has very specific techniques for scratching and marking during sexual encounters. They go beyond what most Westerners might experience, but are titillating nevertheless.

> When love becomes intense, pressing with the nails or scratching the body with them is practiced, and it is done on the following occasions: on the first visit; at the time of setting out on a journey; on the return from a journey; at the time when an angry lover is reconciled; and lastly when the woman is intoxicated.

The most notable thing about this sutra is that the lover about to embark on a journey marks his or her partner with a nail mark that hurts and that lasts. The hurt is to remind the lover of what is left of the passionate moment shared. It is also to show others that their passion is strong.

> But pressing with the nails is not a usual thing except with those who are intensely passionate, i.e. full of passion. It is employed, together with biting, by those to whom the practice is agreeable. Pressing with the nails is of the eight following kinds, according to the forms of the marks that are produced: sounding or limited pressure; half moon or crescent moon shaped; a circular mark or full moon; a straight line; a tiger's nail or claw; a peacock's foot or a five-finger press; the

jump of a hare or the marks of the peacock made close to one another on the breast presses; the leaf or petal of a blue lotus. The places that are to be pressed with the nails are as follows: the arm pit, the throat, the breasts, the lips, the pelvis, or middle parts of the body, and the thighs. But there is the opinion that when the impetuosity of passion is excessive, the places need not be considered.

The Kama Sutra goes on to describe exactly what kinds of nail marks are left on what parts of the body and for what occasions. It is very precise and the marks are highly regarded by both the individual wearing the mark and those that see them upon their bodies. Marks that are left in private places are to remind the wearer of the erotic moment and of their lover.

"The qualities of good nails are that they should be bright, well set, clean, entire, convex, soft, and glossy in appearance." It further says that those with intense passion should file their nails on their left hand in two or three points like the teeth of a saw. Those with a medium passion should file their nails with pointed ends like the beak of a parrot, and those with mild passion should just slightly round their fingernails so that they will produce a crescent shape.

BITING AND EROTIC BLOWS

Love bites are similar to nail marks in that they leave the wearer with a remembrance of the erotic activity that produced them. Nail marks, bites, and blows are all a little difficult to comprehend unless you are of a passionate nature and in the moment of pleasure that masks the intensity of the initial mark. Endorphins, chemical substances in your body that are enhanced when you are sexually excited and that cause euphoria, can mask any pain that occurs during the receiving of the marks. The reminder comes a bit later.

Biting Marks

There are eight kinds of biting marks that are described in the Kama Sutra, and they can be applied to various areas of the body. If a woman is resistant to a man making teeth marks on her but he doesn't stop, she must make even harder, deeper ones on him and in places where they will show to others. "When a man displays the marks made on his body by a woman and then points in her direction, she should simply smile to herself, unobserved by others. She should not be seen smiling even by the man, otherwise both will be considered rustic in manners."

Erotic Blows

"The union of the sexes, by nature, is a combat, offering plenty of scope for differences of opinion. In spite of its tender origin, such love leads to dizzy heights of intense passion, which, in its culmination, becomes blind to the force, and even the pain, of the ways and means used. Accordingly, in a state of high passion, striking or thrashing is considered one of the chief factors for arousing passion, the places most suitable for it being the shoulder, the head, the bosom, the back, the pelvis, and the sides."

Erotic blows, or striking, during love-play are the ultimate in intense passion. The Kama Sutra illustrates the types of blows and the accompanying sounds that might be uttered.

Passionate Actions

In Kama Sutra, Vatsyayana claims that such passionate actions as scratching, marking, biting, and erotic blows, perhaps unacceptable or incomprehensible to some, are all part of the amorous play between lovers.

> *Such passionate actions and amorous gesticulations or movements, which arise on the spur of the moment, and during sexual intercourse, cannot be defined, and are as irregular as dreams. A loving pair can become blind with passion in the heat of congress and go on with great impetuosity, paying not the least regard to excess. For this reason, one who is well acquainted with the science of love, and knowing his own strength as also the tenderness, impetuosity, and strength of the young woman, should act accordingly. The various modes of enjoyment are not for all times or for all persons, but should be enjoyed at the proper times and in the proper places.*

Vatsyayana further states that if a man and woman enjoy their lives and include variations in their lovemaking they will not fall out of love and may be partnered for 100 years. He likens lovemaking to eating. If you eat the same thing day in and day out you will grow very tired of it but if you stay creative and adventurous you will thrive in your love-match.

CHAPTER 11

the art of kissing and oral sex

*h*umans kiss for many different reasons throughout their lives. From a peck to a long, lingering seductive kiss, kisses are used for many varied encounters. Kissing can be the beginning of a sexual encounter or it can be a means to its own end. Whether you put lips to lips, or lips to other body parts, it is an art that can be expanded and refined over a lifetime.

THE NATURE OF OUR MOUTHS

Our mouths are exquisitely erotic, though few of us stop to think about it. We take for granted the tender tissues, sensitive nerve endings, and gymnastic capabilities of our tongues. We forget that even our food is sensuous and that eating (tasting) can be erotic. Along with the sense of smell, it is one of our senses that we take for granted when making love.

The ability to form words and have a developed language is uniquely human. That capacity has helped create a structure to our mouths that makes them very versatile. The muscles that control the tongue, lips, and whole mouth structure give us the ability to have great sensitivity and strength in that area. This all adds up to an exquisitely erotic organ that can serve you well in your lovemaking.

THE KISS

The pleasurable release of endorphins that accompanies deep, erotic kissing begins the flood of chemicals that readies you for sexual contact. When you are very close to someone and start kissing him, you come in contact with the odorless compounds of pheromones. Pheromones are the sexual attractants that draw us to each other. They are powerful chemicals that are produced in our sweat glands and other areas of our skin.

One time when kissing belongs is after climax when both of you may feel satiated. It is a bonding experience that should not be overlooked. Many women say that they miss this part at the end of lovemaking and wish their partners were more interested in it. It brings a sense of closeness, comfort, and closure to a wonderful experience.

Spending an hour kissing with your partner is a rare treat that you may not think is "enough," but as a sensual activity it can really get you turned on. At other times, kissing is the prelude to other sexual activities that may lead to intercourse. This would include oral sex. Using your mouth to kiss and caress your lover's body all over is a very erotic experience. Kissing, licking, blowing warm air, and even light sucking on the neck, face, and other areas add to the sensuous arousal.

THE TREATISE ON KISSING

The *Treatise on Kissing* from the Kama Sutra covers the kinds of kisses you can use, the places on the body that the kisses should be placed, and the ways of kissing people who have never been kissed before. It also covers the arts relating to oral sex or oral kissing, as it's called in the Kama Sutra, for both men and women. It is descriptive and includes biting, scratching, and the order in which actions should occur. Vatsyayana concludes, pragmatically, that when passion takes over there are no right or wrong ways to anything pertaining to lovemaking!

It is said by some that there is no fixed time or order between the embrace, the kiss, and the pressing or scratching with the nails or fingers, but that all these things should be done generally before sexual union takes place, while striking and making the various sounds generally takes place at the time of the union. Vatsyayana, however, thinks that anything may take place at any time, for love does not care for time or order.

On the occasion of the first congress, kissing and the other things mentioned above should be done moderately, they should not be continued for a long time, and should be done alternately. On subsequent occasions, however, the reverse of all this may take place, and moderation will not be necessary, they may continue for a long time, and, for the purpose of kindling love, they may be all done at the same time.

Places for Kissing

The Kama Sutra lists the places on the body that are most suitable for kissing. These places correspond to some of the primary and secondary erogenous zones spread out over the surface of the body. These are the forehead, the eyes, the cheeks, the throat, the bosom, the breasts, the lips, and the interior of the mouth.

Other erogenous zones are the joints of the thighs, the arms, and the navel. It is well known that the inner thighs, the back of the knees and elbows, and the sides of the torso are very sensitive.

Four Kinds of Kisses

The Kama Sutra describes four kinds of kisses, which get progressively more erotic and forceful. They are the straight kiss, the bent kiss, the turned kiss, and the pressed kiss. Try each of these in turn and find your own variations on them.

1. "The straight kiss results when simply the lips are in contact, facing each other."

2. "The slanting kiss requires one of the participants to slant the kissing lips diagonally against the other's lips."

3. "The turned is effected when one of the two lovers turns up the face of the other by holding the head and the chin, and then kisses."

4. "The pressed kiss takes place when any of the three varieties mentioned above is done with some force."

According to the Kama Sutra, these four kinds of kisses can also be done in two different ways: there is the pure kiss, when only the lips are used to do the kissing; and the tongue kiss, where the tips of the tongues come into play. So-called "French kissing" would call for the whole tongue to be used to investigate the far corners of the mouth. This might include the areas around the teeth, inside the lips, and the upper palate. The upper palate is very nerve sensitive and quite erotic. Usually deep tongue kissing comes a little later as the erotic charge and desire builds to it.

There is also a fifth kind of kiss that the Kama Sutra lists: "Holding the lower lip with the thumb and index finger, and shaping it to an 'O,' and then kissing it with the lips only, without using the teeth". Try it.

A LESSON IN KISSING

Our lips are extremely sensitive and receptive to stimulation. Many people hold their lips rather stiffly, not allowing them to be relaxed and open to the receiving and giving required for good kissing. You might want to practice using your lips in more soft and open ways. Parting them slightly and keeping them moist gives an alluring appeal. This will also heighten their sensitivity.

Practice pouting softly when you are by yourself to relax the lips and expose more of the fleshy interior. In general, become more aware of your lips. Try eating your meals slower than you might usually, and really feel the food passing between your lips. You can practice sucking on soft fruit, such as a piece of mango or banana, for the sensual affect it has on your mouth and lips.

When you are about to kiss, lick your lips to wet them, open your mouth a little way, tip your head very slightly, and go softly forward. Leave your tongue out of it for now. Gently explore the interior of your partner's lips with your lips. Move very slowly but with confidence. Go deeper, and open your mouth a bit more as you feel yourself moving into the kiss. Create a slight amount of suction as you expand and open your mouth a little bigger.

Love and pleasure – what is your capacity? If you're exploring the practices in this book, you'll begin to transform the amount of pleasure you can receive. As a result, you'll expand the pleasure you give to others, too. Remind yourself often that you can receive more pleasure.

You can suck on the lower lip, the upper lip, and the corners of the lips. You can cover the same areas with light bites that include a little suction. Take your lover's whole mouth into yours. Do this lovingly, as if you are exploring it for the first time. Then, eat them up, but gently. Tease. Let them tease. The subtler you are with this, the better. Kissing can go on for a long time if it's treated playfully and erotically.

THE ART OF FELLATIO

The art of giving oral sex has come in and out of favor over the millennia – depending on which culture one might make reference to. During the eras that the Kama Sutra was written, it was thought that oral sex was debasing, yet many people enjoyed it. The face was considered beautiful and morally "clean," and to have genitals touch it was considered wrong. Yet, it appears everyone was doing it!

Behave According to Your Inclinations

The Kama Sutra does go on to instruct in this fine art. Vatsayanya is liberal in his interpretation, saying: "Opinions differ on the matter of purity between the authority of the moral codes, occasional local customs, and one's own feelings. One should therefore behave according to one's inclinations".

It's curious to consider why there might have been restrictions during a time when generally the attitudes about sexual loving were quite liberal. Speculation on the subject might include that the contraction of illnesses and diseases was worrisome. It might also have been that by having only oral sex, a young woman of the times might get away with having unmarried sex yet, technically, still be a virgin.

Techniques on Kissing the Lingam

Fellatio is the term used for giving pleasure to the male's genitals with the mouth and tongue. Root words from the Latin include references to "swollen" and "sucking." Here are the various techniques to consider when considering the art of fellatio:

- **Touching**: "When your lover catches your penis in her hand and, shaping her lips to an 'O,' lays them lightly to its tip, moving her head in tiny circles, this is the first step."
- **Biting at the Sides**: "Next, grasping its head in her hand, she clamps her lips tightly about the shaft, first on one side then the other, taking great care that her teeth don't hurt you."
- **The Outer Pincers**: "Now she takes the head of your penis gently between her lips, by turns pressing, kissing it tenderly and pulling at its soft skin."
- **The Inner Pincers**: "Next she allows the head to slide completely into her mouth and presses the shaft firmly between her lips, holding a moment before pulling away."
- **Kissing**: "Taking your penis in her hand and making her lips very round, she presses fierce kisses along its whole length, sucking as she would at your lower lip."
- **Striking at the Tip**: "While kissing, she lets her tongue flick all over your penis and then, pointing it, strikes repeatedly at the sensitive glans and tip."

- **Sucking a Mango**: "Now, fired by passion, she takes your penis deep into her mouth, pulling upon it and sucking as vigorously as though she were stripping clean a mango seed."
- **Swallowed Whole**: "When she senses that your orgasm is imminent she swallows up the whole penis, sucking and working upon it with lips and tongue until you are spent."

Ejaculation Mastery

More will be said about ejaculation mastery in a later chapter but it's important to add a note here. The giver usually controls the outcome of the oral sex experience when the man is receiving. More often than not the giver thinks that she is really good when she takes her lover over the top quickly. You are doing your lover and yourself an injustice if you do this.

Don't try to control the situation like that. Along with quick self-pleasuring, this is the way men get trained to go over the top too quickly. Train them to last a long time by "peaking" them, having them relax between peaks, and then repeating. Your man will quickly learn to last longer while you're both having fun!

Things to Remember

There's something mysterious and forbidden about oral sex, yet it's desirability cannot be denied. The control and surrender, the visual aspects for the couple, and the vulnerable nature of an act that has had a history of shame surrounding it are powerful motivators. It can often be a source of struggle for couples when one partner wants it and the other does not want to give it or get it.

When men voice their sexual fantasies and dreams, they often contain elements of oral sex. This has been true for so long that it's covered in the Kama Sutra and earlier texts, such as the Kama Shastra. When both partners really enjoy giving and receiving oral sex, it is an erotic and arousing addition to lovemaking.

Remember, confidence, not techniques, is the ultimate sensual driver. You can build confidence by knowing you are doing something that turns you on, and that you want to be doing it. It's nice to know techniques but wanting to explore, have fun, and pleasure your partner are the most important parts of this intimate journey.

The Act

Start by using your fingers to softly and tenderly brush the hair near and around, but not on, his "jewels" (the erotic adventurers of the past liked to call the genitals of both men and women by symbolic names). Gently tease, pull, and even nibble bits of the hair. You might try blowing your warm breath over the area. Move slowly but deliberately.

As you tease and excite him, place light kisses on his inner thighs, below his navel, and then zero in on the base of his penis. Work your way up to the head, placing kisses along the way. At this point, wet your lips and, as gently as you can, take the *lingam* into your mouth.

It's always very yummy to begin with a "soft-on." As you feel the lingam *growing, you can create a little more suction with your mouth. Put attention on the feedback loop that is created between you, your sensations, then his sensations – back and forth. Pay attention to this because, if you are new to this, it will help you enjoy the experience more.*

Notice the sensations in your upper palate. How does your mouth feel? Is it soft and wet? Are you thinking versus feeling your own pleasure? There is an energetic, and possibly physical, connection between the upper palate in the mouth and the G-spot in women. Really focus on how good this feels to your mouth and your partner is going to have a great time!

There are as many variations on how to give oral sex as there are people to give it. Focus more on fun, exploration, and variety. Don't move too fast or make too many different moves in a short period of time. Use your hands at the same time you are using your mouth. You can add a variety of strokes like pulling down on his shaft while pulling up with your mouth, or cup and gently pull his scrotum as you pleasure him with your mouth.

woman-on-top positions

*T*he Kama Sutra refers to woman-on-top positions as "woman assuming the man's role." It treats the subject with a delicious intrigue and obvious support. Though the chapter can be translated several ways, as you'll soon see, the underlying factor is apparent – when passion ignites there is no stopping even a bashful girl. All is truly fair in love and war.

THE NATURE OF AN EROTIC WOMAN

Empowering, satisfying, vulnerable, creative, and edgy – all these adjectives and more can be applied to positions where the woman is acting the role of the man – or "on top," in more modern terms. Sometimes women want to be "controlled" and sometimes they want to "control." Assuming the top position can have the effect of bringing out the powerful "animal passion" in any woman. It's a wonderful lover who will allow his woman her full repertoire of sexual expression.

A Historical Perspective

Many cultures of the past have kept women in a very subservient role. The relationship between men and women depended on the two having distinctly separate identities. Women were often accused of being in liege with the devil when they showed tendencies toward powerful sexual urges – and even when those urges were with their husbands behind their own bedroom doors. Sexual energy was repressed in women.

Women can help their men last longer during sex. By playing the roll of the sexual initiator and encouraging position changes during lovemaking, you can slow things down for your man. Pay attention to his breath and movements to know when to initiate a shift in positions.

The society at the time of the Kama Sutra honored a woman's sexual urges and honored courtesans as well. They were considered "wives of the city" and were respected by all. The idea that each man and woman also contained a balance of the other's energy pervaded the philosophy of the times. The principle of the yin/yang considers that every individual contains both male and female characteristics, and that these should be developed inside of each of us as fully as possible.

Role Reversal

Role reversal is not only a fabulously fun thing to do while having sex, but it also allows the woman an outlet for that expression she isn't often afforded in other ways in life. The woman as leader in the sexual role means that the man must take a back seat for a while. Her energy is driving the experience, and that means that he must give up control. This can be difficult for some men, but makes it all the more important as a life lesson. It is often women themselves who hold themselves back by keeping in line with social mores. It's difficult to overcome the training that our families, churches, communities, and cultures might have put us through. Personal fears often keep women from exploring a fuller range of possibility when it comes to sexuality.

If you haven't tried any of the "top positions," now is the time to try. Be gentle with yourself, and be sure to tell your partner of any vulnerable feelings you are experiencing.

"When a woman sees her lover is fatigued by constant congress, without having his or her desire satisfied, she should, with his permission, lay him down upon his back, and give him assistance by acting his part. She may also do this to satisfy the curiosity of her lover, or her own desire for novelty". The sutras say that the woman may either start the lovemaking this way or the couple may move into these positions in due course. However, she should take care not to let slip the man's *lingam* from the Love Temple. "She climbs upon you, the flowers dropping from her tousled hair, her giggles turning to gasps; every time she bends to kiss your lips her nipples pierce your chest."

All Is Fair in Love and War

The Kama Sutra actually encouraged women to be forceful in their passionate pursuits. It details when and how a woman might get back at her lover when she is angry or even pretending anger. Love was thought of as a sort of sport (or game) to be played and all was fair as long as no one got physically hurt. If feelings were hurt, they got mended before the love play was complete.

"As her hips begin to churn, her head, flung back, bobs ever faster; she scratches, pummels you with small fists, fastens her teeth in your neck, doing unto you what you have often done unto her". If her partner thought to put love marks on her, like bites and scratches, then she was encouraged to return the marks. "Though a woman may be reserved and try to hide her feelings and desires, she cannot successfully do so when she assumes the role of the man through intense passion."

Erotic Stimulation

The basic configuration for the range of woman-on-top positions is for the man to be lying on his back and the woman to straddle him. She can be facing forward, sideways, or backward. The majority of these positions call for the woman to be facing forward for eye contact, kissing, and speaking. Both partners' hands are free to caress, fondle, and rub different parts of the other partner's body. Experiment with moving your legs to one side or the other while riding your partner. One knee up, one knee down, then switching, is a great combination.

The face-to-face positions are also the best for G-spot stimulation. As a woman, you can control the depth of thrusting to place the *lingam* in just the right spot for your best stimulation. Whether you like deep, shallow, or a combination of thrusting, you can facilitate your own experience by being on top.

FACE-TO-FACE POSITIONS

Face-to-face positions are the most intimate of the woman-on-top positions. Both lovers can see each other to kiss and speak. They can witness each other's powerful erotic nature and see the beauty each other has. The flush of the skin, the tiny jewel drops of perspiration, the softly glowing eyes of the lover are all precious visuals that keep the couple engaged and aroused in love-play.

Variations on the Prime Position

Both the Kama Sutra and the Ananga Ranga bring you a variety of positions to fuel your passion and imagination. When astride your partner, try leaning down on top of his chest with your knees on the bed. This particular position is a good one for clitoral stimulation because the two of you can rub against each other. With your hands under his shoulders, you can guide your lover in the speed of rubbing to apply maximum friction where you need it most. This is one of the only positions where you can get direct stimulation of the clitoris without the use of the hands.

With your knees on the bed, sit up on your lover. There is a great range of motion with this position because you can move up and down on your partner, as well as forward and backward. Use your hands to apply pressure to your lover's chest for movement, and also caress your lover's face and body.

"When the woman swings her hips and abdomen on all sides, including back and forth and side to side or in circular movements, it is called The Swing". This movement is like a belly dancer's hips swaying. You can practice belly dance moves on your own and then bring your hips back to the bedroom to try the moves out. These movements can be used in a great variety of situations to add stimulus and imagination to your lovemaking.

Try putting your feet on the bed as you sit astride your lover. This allows you to raise and lower yourself onto your partner. The Kama Sutra calls this position the "Fluttering and Soaring Butterfly" because the woman is in control of the rhythm, depth of thrusting, speed, and angle of penetration. It takes strong thighs to maintain it for any length of time. The man can use his hands to help support the woman and guide her timing.

Next, try one leg with the foot on the bed and the other with the knee on the bed. This position is useful when a woman likes one side of her vagina or G-spot stimulated more than another. It's also very powerful for you to put your hand under your lover's buttocks on the side with the foot on the bed. Pull him gently closer and rock him back and forth. Try both sides.

Unique Positions from the Old Texts

Both of the well-known Indian erotic texts contain unique postures with evocative names. Notice in some of them the use of animal names and plant references. Drawing comparisons to nature is a wonderful practice that the Asian love arts did well. Here are a few:

- "If, drawing up her feet, she revolves her hips so that your penis circles deep within her yoni, you arching your body to help her, it is The Bee."
- "Catching your penis, the lady with dark eyes like upturned lotus petals guides it into her yoni, clings to you and shakes her buttocks: this is Lovely Lady in Control."
- "Enthroned on your penis, she places both hands on the bed and makes love, while you press your two hands to her thudding heart: this is Seat of Sport."
- "Clasping each other's hands, you lie sprawled like two starfish making love, her breasts stabbing your chest, her thighs stretched out along yours: this is The Coitus of the Gods."

FACE-TO-FEET POSITIONS

Some women and men like these positions because of the view they offer to the man. They aren't as effective in reaching the G-spot, but they are great for deeper thrusting for women who like to have the cervix area stimulated during intercourse. They can be intimate when the variations used are the ones where both are sitting, and the man holds the woman close as she sits on his lap. They are especially good if you hang a mirror on the wall so that the two of you can see yourselves.

Here are a few:

- "If you lie flat on your back with legs stretched out and your lover sits astride you, facing away and grasping your feet, it is called The Bull."
- "If she strides you, facing your feet, brings both her feet up to your thighs, and works her hips frantically, it is known as Swan Sport."
- "Your lover places one foot on your ankle, lodges her other foot just above your knee, and rides you, swinging and rotating her hips, it is known as Garuda – the Bird."

In many of these positions, the woman can place her feet or her knees on the bed. Try the one-foot and one-knee stance as in the front-facing positions. Lean forward or backward for more variety and G-spot stimulation.

CHALLENGING POSITIONS

The more challenging positions can be a lot of fun to try when the two of you are in a light mood and ready for some adventure. It will help to be very limber and to have a few big pillows around for extra support when needed. Be careful when trying some of these – don't fall off the bed.

Many of these positions are from another well-known Hindu love manual called the Ananga Ranga, which was also translated by Sir Richard Burton of England. Throughout the ages, the love postures from both the Ananga Ranga and the

Kama Sutra have been intertwined. Their addition here gives a much deeper background of information. Some are very interesting indeed.

Women, when you are on top, remember to be careful with your partner's lingam. *In your enthusiasm you'll need to make sure that you don't damage it by bouncing down too hard. If it gets caught a little off center and you bend it, it can cause damage to the sensitive blood-holding regions. Play it safe by keeping it in the* yoni.

The Swan

"She sits upright upon you, her head thrown back like a rearing mare, bringing her feet together on the bed to one side of your body: this is called The Swan." Depending on which side you might put your two legs, this position could greatly affect your G-spot. You'll need to use your hands to support yourself and to be able to move up and down on your partner.

The Sacred Thread and Reversed

"The young woman has one foot on your heart and the other on the bed. Bold, saucy women adore this posture, which is known to the world as The Sacred Thread." This is a wonderful name. It is derived from the fact that the woman is making a sacred connection with her foot to the man's heart. This connects them and binds the love and other-worldliness of the sexual union.

The man can help in any of the woman-superior positions by cupping his hands under your buttocks and lifting you up and down. It's fun to have the help and the two of you can dance in the interplay of figuring out the rhythm and speed. It is especially appreciated when your thighs get tired.

"If, with one of her feet clasped in your hand and the second placed upon your shoulder, your young lady enjoys you, it is called Reversed." This is a hard position to understand. If you try it be careful!

The Foot Yoke
"If your lover, seated above you with feet lotus-crossed and her body held erect and still makes love to you, it is known as The Foot Yoke." You will definitely need your partner to help you move up and down with this position. Just getting into the Lotus Position on top of your lover while he keeps his erection is challenging. Your love muscles will need to be in great shape for this one.

The Wheel
"Lying upon you, your beloved moves round like a wheel, pressing hands one after the other on the bed, kissing your body as she circles: experts call this The Wheel." This posture or position is similar to "the Foot Yoke" except that the woman lies down on the man when she moves all the way around him. Positions like these can hurt the woman if she isn't careful about the angle that the penis is penetrating the

vagina. Sometimes the male/female combination that you and your partner make isn't conducive to this kind of movement. It can hurt the woman by having the insides of her *yoni* bumped by the *lingam* at certain angles.

WOMEN'S WORRIES

Many women say that they avoid being on top because they don't feel confident about how their bodies look. They believe that their breasts sag or their tummy is the first thing their man sees. They worry about the children coming in, or the phone ringing, or that they might crush their partners. The worrying gives them the excuse to not take the initiative. Control can be a little frightening.

The Kama Sutra repeats often that once lovemaking commences, all rules and sutras fly out the door. Let that happen to you when you make love. Abandon inhibitions that keep you from trying erotic new ideas.

Body Issues

Men love breasts hanging in their visual field. If you are really worried, try some positions early on that don't let your breasts hang as much. The positions where the woman puts both of her feet on the bed or floor, on either side of the man, are good because your body is more upright and your knees keep your breasts from hanging. This position takes very strong legs, though, to maintain it for any length of time.

Eventually, you'll need to just trust that your lover wants to see your body and thinks it is beautiful.

The Everyday Worries

Women worry about different things than men. While men tend to worry about things such as work, being a good provider, and being a virile lover, women often worry about the children, if the oven got turned off, what someone might think of her, do her thighs jiggle, and whether she is being a good lover.

There really aren't many "right" things when it comes to sex, though. Fun, depth, adventure, and losing oneself in union with the other are all the right things, not techniques. When you practice focusing on pleasurable sensations in yourself, you'll get out of your head and into the bed.

TRICKS AND TREATS

The woman superior positions allow you to maneuver your hips, thighs, upper body, and *yoni* muscles to bring great pleasure to both yourself and your lover. This movement can occur as wild, energetic thrusting, or quiet, subtle actions that stem from the squeezing of the love muscles — or a combination of both. The sexually experienced woman can bring heightened pleasure to a union by practicing these skills and allowing herself the freedom to assume the control at times during lovemaking.

"When she takes the man's role, your lady has the choice of three famous lovemaking techniques: The Tongs, The

Spinning of the Top, and The Swing. These techniques can be used with other positions while the woman is on top. Strong PC (pubococcygeus) muscles will provide any woman with the skills to add variety and excitement to any positions or situation.

Using will and intent in your life can help you have a better sex life! Also, cultivating intention can lead to a more satisfying sex life. Start by focusing on the little things in life and developing skills that keep you moving toward what you want out of life.

"If she uses the Mare's Trick, gripping your penis with her yoni's vice, squeezing and stroking it, holding it inside her for a hundred heartbeats, it is known as The Tongs"; "When, while engaged in congress, she turns round and round like a wheel, it is called The Spinning of the Top." This move requires a lot of practice and the woman needs to be small in size. She supports herself and moves around the man with pressure on his chest and legs. "When the woman swings her hips and abdomen on all sides, including back and forth and side to side or in circular movements, it is called The Swing."

All of these variations can be easily moved through, like a dance, as the lovemaking progresses. You can perfect this dance by staying aware, limber, and by sometimes leading and sometimes letting your partner lead. Remember to use your hands liberally to caress and fondle your partner.

rear-entry positions

Without a doubt the rear-entry is one of the best sets of sexual positions. The Kama Sutra thought highly of nature and so the text suggested that erotic explorers study animals' ways of lovemaking. The rear-entry positions are the result of those studies, with added sophistication from thousands of years of further research.

ANIMAL-LIKE BEHAVIOR IN BED

There is a certain stigmatism about the more "animal-like" behaviors during sex, for some people. For whatever reasons – societal, parental, or maybe an experience that didn't go well – you may be reluctant to attempt some of these. Try suspending your judgments sometime soon and invite your lover to an evening of adventure.

Advantages Galore

Rear-entry positions enhance G-spot stimulation. They have the advantage of leaving the hands free to caress and **140** fondle the breasts, buttocks, and back. Variety is easy to come by in these positions, too.

You can adjust the angle and depth of penetration and the ways you move. This allows the woman to tailor-make the experience for herself while having a lot of room to increase the pleasure for her partner. It also enables the woman or the man to stimulate her clitoris. For some women, this is an important part of intercourse.

Men may find increased control in these positions, which will assist them in lasting longer. They can be in control of the depth, speed, and rhythm. They have a wonderful, archetypal view of their partner. Men can feel powerful and still maintain sensitivity with their partner.

Choosing the Right Time

Rear-entry positions aren't always the most appropriate, however. The moment must be right. Sometimes it's just more appropriate to be facing each other. Eye contact, breath connection, heart connection, and intimacy are all facilitated through facing your partner.

If either of you has issues or is sensitive about trying some of these positions, you'll need to talk. Be open with each other and vulnerable when you speak. If you are, your partner will hear you better and be more compassionate. Even with reservations, try a few of these. If you have to push yourself over the edge a little, know that it's a good learning experience. You may love it.

TYPES OF REAR-ENTRY POSITIONS

The Kama Sutra names the rear-entry positions after animals, as this is their natural source. This adds a creative, evocative essence to them. It even goes as far as to suggest that couples mimic the sounds and attitudes of the animals that inspired the position.

The Deer

"If the lady, eager for love, goes on all fours, humping her back like a doe, and you enjoy her from behind, rutting as though you'd lost all human nature, it is called: The Deer." Try this position first with both partners on their knees. It's best for the woman to support herself with both her hands, on all fours, so that she can keep her spine moving and undulating. Use the different rhythms and depths of penetration to explore how this basic position feels to both of you.

A great variation on this position is for the woman to lift one of her legs so that her lover can hold it up for her. Alternate lifting each leg as one will most likely be more effective than the other. Make a study of how it feels, and communicate your findings to your lover for future reference.

The Dog

"If you mount her like a dog, gripping her waist, and she twists round to gaze into your face, experts in the art of love say it is: The Dog." The variations on all of these positions lend themselves well to different locations around the house and yard. Try this position on a padded chair or couch.

The Elephant

"When your mistress lays breasts, arms, and forehead to the carpet, raising her buttocks high, and you guide your penis into her yoni, it is called: The Elephant." Though this isn't a great G-spot position, it has many advantages. It is restful and comfortable, and also very erotic. If you like your partner to play with and stimulate your anal area, this is a great position.

This is also a good position for stimulating the man by caressing his scrotum or his inner thighs. You can help him stay focused on non-ejaculatory pleasure by cupping his scrotum in your hands and gently applying pressure with a downward pull. You can apply pressure to his perineum area also, which is the exterior access to his prostate gland.

The "love handles," or waistline area of the torso, are exquisite erogenous zones. Hold on here often and even caress the sides of the torso from under the arms all the way down the sides to the hips. Holding on firmly in this area, to facilitate thrusting, is very erotic for both the man and the woman.

The Reverse-Monkey Position

"The round-thighed woman on the bed grasps her ankles and raises high her lotus feet; you strike her to the root, kissing and slapping open-palmed between her breasts – this is The Monkey." A much easier variation on this position has the man sit back on his thighs and the woman sit back on top of him, still in the rear-entry position.

SOME DIFFERENT MODALITIES TO TRY

Try pumping and squeezing your PC muscles in some of these positions. Both of you can do this to see how it feels. Try breathing in-sync and squeezing together. Keep a small hand mirror available somewhere near your bed so that the two of you can eye gaze as you get more and more aroused.

Ask yourselves how you are doing often when trying new positions. Don't assume that your partner is having a good time without asking. When you try new things ask: "What has changed?" Both of you take notice of any subtle changes. Is your G-spot as stimulated in this position? Do you find it easier to rise up and down on your partner? What do you notice in each of these?

STANDING REAR-ENTRY POSITIONS

The Kama Sutra makes note of just one rear-entry position. "When a woman stands on her hands and feet like a quadruped, and her lover mounts her like a bull, it is called: the Congress of the Cow. At this time everything that is ordinarily done on the bosom should be done on the back". It then goes on to say, "In the same way can be carried on the congress of the dog, the congress of the goat, the congress of a deer, the forcible mounting of an ass, the congress of a cat, the jump of a tiger, the pressing of an elephant, the rubbing of a boar, and the mounting of a horse. And in all of these the characteristics of the different animals should be manifested by acting like them."

The Lending-an-Arm Position

The couch or overstuffed chair will always be more than happy to lend you an arm. Lean over the arm as you stand on the floor. Your lover will stand behind you. You can also try kneeling on both knees on the chair near the edge.

The Stork

Try a standing position next to the arm of a comfortable chair by holding on to the chair arm, bending over slightly, and lifting either your right or left leg into the air while your lover enters you. Lift your leg straight back behind you so that your lover can hold it by his side and use it as a lever arm to move you to and fro. Experiment with different legs held high and then low. You'll probably find that one of your legs is better than the other. You'll notice more friction in just the area you need it on your G-spot.

The Ass

"When, with lotus-feet set well-apart on the ground, she bends, placing a hand upon each thigh, and you take her from the rear, it is called: The Ass." The man should caress and hold the woman's waist so that she doesn't fall forward in this position. This position takes a strong limber body.

Rear-entry positions are excellent G-spot stimulating positions. Because both partners can maneuver their bodies so well, access to the G-spot can become very precise.

TRICKS AND TIPS

For the very erotic couple, these positions will be exciting. You'll be able to find subtle variations that will suit you as a couple and add new, creative extras to get even more out of this group of love postures. Here are a few tips to help you fantasize and get your creative juices started:

The Mirror

In the past, couples have used mirrors for a variety of reasons during lovemaking. They can be seen in old Chinese Taoist drawings being used by couples that wished to study their faces while in orgasmic pleasure. The Taoists felt that is was important to be able to witness oneself in the act of pleasure in order to understand better the nature of one's own bliss.

You can use a hand mirror or mount one or two mirrors on your bedroom walls. The hand mirror is intimate because you can pick it up and have it very close to your faces. In rear-entry positions you can both look into it and see each other. It makes a very exciting and intimate picture of the two of you.

The Bed Bar

Using a bar suspended above the bed or using a high headboard can be erotic and fun when trying rear-entry positions. If you can get a higher angle on the *lingam* inside of you by holding yourself up on the headboard or bar, you can put more stimulation on your G-spot. You can also assist your man in thrusting because you can pull herself up and down with your hands.

Involving the Scrotum in Lovemaking

Many men love to have their scrotum gently pulled during lovemaking because it can help them control their ejaculation and will add increased pleasure to the experience. But it is often difficult to get into a position that allows this kind of activity. Some of the rear-entry postures make it easier to reach his genitals for this stimulating addition.

Be gentle and always ask first if it is something he would like to try. You may also wish to apply pressure to his perineum (the external area between the anus and the scrotum that covers his prostate gland or the male G-spot). This will help keep him from going over the top, so to speak.

Another option is to tie a very slim silk belt or robe tie around his scrotum with a slipknot. String it forward, between his legs, and hold onto it. Gently tug and pull on it to increase the pressure and pull on his scrotum.

CHAPTER 14

sitting, lying and standing positions

Some of the most sublime, challenging, and relaxing positions can be found in this group of ancient lovemaking postures. From the transformational Tantric Yab/Yum to the mythical standing positions that only a few will try – all are out of the ordinary and extraordinary too. Using your mind to help your body get into some of these positions will help you feel the soul in them.

CONSCIOUSNESS AND SEX

Bringing consciousness to sex isn't something that you are probably used to thinking about. Ancient lovers and philosophers thought otherwise. They believed that through sexuality a person could gain valuable skills and insight into the mind, body, and spirit. Some of the more experimental positions give the opportunity for a couple to stay really tuned in to what they are doing.

It may be easy for you to have pretty good sex by using three or four main positions during intercourse that are familiar to you and your partner. Trying new positions, though, is on the top of the list for most couples that are looking for a new lift to their sex lives. If this is you, you are on the right track.

Positions that are new to you and your partner tend to make you sit up and think a little. You get more conscious. Sometimes you have to use your mind to figure out where a leg goes or what angle is best for stimulation. You have to be more involved than going on habitual behavior. This is always good for a relationship.

Make a list of four new positions from this chapter that appeal to you. If you are the more cautious one in the relationship, then pick the order that you will try them in. If you are the more adventurous, then let your partner design the order and even pick the positions. Let that person be the leader in this love game.

If you are afraid of trying new things during sex, but your partner wants to, then try a new position or two. It is the easiest and most fun way to explore new territory in a sexual relationship. Start with easier ones and then move into a few more advanced ones. Stay light, stay alert, and have fun.

SITTING POSITIONS

"Sitting erect, grip your lover's waist and pull her on to you, your loins continuously leaping together with a sound like the flapping of elephants' ears: this is called: The Knot of Fame"

(The Ananga Ranga). There are only a few actual sitting positions, but they are gems. The ancient Tantric experts claimed these positions aided in the movement of conscious energy that kept the body healthy and connected them to the gods and goddesses.

Here are examples of a few sitting positions from the Kama Sutra and the Ananga Ranga:

- "Seated, mouth to mouth, arms against arms, thighs against thighs, this is: The Tortoise."
- "If the lovers' thighs, still joined, are raised, it is called: Turning."
- "If, within the cave of her thighs, you sit rotating your hips like a black bee, it is: The Monkey."
- "And if, in this pose, you turn away from her, it is called: Crushing Spices."
- "When your wife sits with both knees drawn tight to her body and you mirror this posture, it is known to experts in the art of love as: The Foot Yoke."
- "Seated erect, the lovely girl folds one leg to her body and stretches the other along the bed, while you mirror her actions: this is: The Feet Yoke."

Yab-Yum Position

The Yab-Yum Position is a little known, but excellent position from the Tantric tradition of India. Lovers sit upon each other face-to-face and heart-to-heart. They are able to keep eye contact, kiss, and caress each other. This position is the best one for extending the sexual experience because it prevents the man from thrusting so much that he ejaculates too quickly. It allows for the deep connection that makes the extended lovemaking experience magical.

In this position, the man sits cross-legged on the bed or floor, and the woman sits astride him. She is facing him and has her legs wrapped around him with the souls of her feet coming together behind him. Both partners have their arms and hands wrapped around the backs of their partner. Their faces are very close. The woman can also put a firm pillow under her buttocks to help with the pressure on her lover's thighs.

The lovers are sitting up, in an "awake" position, versus lying down. With the man's penis in the "up" position, the whole energy is vertical. This allows the couple's bodies to move and wave in a freer manner. The breath of each partner can move in synchronicity or they can do alternate breathing for maximum pheromone transmission. The hands of each partner support the other and the man can easily control his urge to ejaculate.

In the classic Yab-Yum Position, the woman can lean back on pillows and relax as her partner uses his hands to bring her closer for thrusting. His hands are available to caress her clitoris and massage her breasts and thighs.

This is a great position to use when the man starts getting too close to ejaculation. It's a position that is easy for the man to stay aroused in even when there is a minimum of movement. By combining fast, hot movements with slow, steady rocking, and even stillness, a dance can be created. This allows you to remain in a high state of ecstatic connection for virtually as long as you want.

The Classic Hassock Yab-Yum

You can modify the Yab-Yum posture so that you are really comfortable. If you are unable to do the yogic, cross-legged version of this position, here's another version. You can create the same effect by having the man sit on the edge of the bed or a padded hassock (footstool) with his legs on the floor while the woman sits facing him on his lap. Make sure the man's legs are parallel to the floor from the knees to the hip. This is a good modification for people with lower back problems.

Making Love Like Moths

A Tantric lying-down position that makes reference to moths making love also looks like a Yantra, or Tantric magical symbol. The couple lies down on their backs with the souls of their feet touching, holding their legs in the crooks of their arms. They are close together with buttock touching and the man's *lingam* in the woman's *yoni*.

This is a difficult position and one that requires both partners to be very limber. It may be much easier to start in a sitting position and then recline backward to the lying-down position. Another option is to have just one of you lie back while the other stays sitting. The sitting partner can use his or her hands to caress all the parts of the other partner's body from this position.

Squatting Position

The man must have very strong, limber leg muscles for this one. He squats and she sits astride him, facing him. Her legs are left dangling in air as he supports her. The woman can hold her legs in the crook of her arms, too. He can hold on to a bar or couch arm to help steady them. Subtle movements and rocking achieve the couple's ecstasy.

STANDING POSITIONS

These are the positions that seem mythological and impossible to even think of trying. You may be inclined to skip right over this section but don't be too sure that there isn't something available to you and your partner, even modified, that might suit you very well in your lovemaking quest.

Some of these positions require that you and your partner be of similar heights so that your genitals will meet. However, in others, where the woman is lifted up, your height won't matter.

Supported Congress

"When a couple make love standing, or leaning against a wall or a pillar, it is called Supported Congress". Leaning on a wall will make this position much easier to try. You might even want to cheat a little and sit on bar stool next to the wall. Then your lover can lift you up from that height as he gets more turned on you trust he's actually got you in his arms.

Suspended Congress

"When the woman sits in her lover's cradled hands, her arms around his neck, thighs gripping his waist, her feet pushing back and forth against a wall, it is: Suspended." In this posture, the man stands against a wall or anything that will support his back, and the woman sits on his clasped hands as he holds her up. Again, you may want to start from a bar stool or table-top. She is suspended by his arms and holds herself to him with her own arms around his neck and her legs around his thighs. If you are small, you can thrust by pushing your feet against the wall that is supporting the man.

STANDING POSITIONS FROM THE ANANGA RANGA

The Ananga Ranga, which was a later love manual from India (translated into English by Sir Richard Burton in the 1800s), names additional standing lovemaking postures to the ones the Kama Sutra details. The Kama Sutra is actually a little lean on positions. The Ananga Ranga was used by couples in ancient India as an adjunct to the Kama Sutra. Here are some examples of standing positions from the Ananga Ranga:

- "When, catching and crushing your lover in the cage of your arms, you force her knees apart with yours and sink slowly into her, it is called: Churning Curds." This is a standing position but the activity is more of a thrusting technique than an actual position. In certain standing postures the man has a lot of leeway to move his hips to simulate the Churning Curds.

- "When she leans against a wall, planting her feet as widely apart as possible, and you enter the cave between her thighs, eager for lovemaking, it is: Face-to-Face." You'll both need to be about the same height. Try it from a sitting position, too, by having the man sit on a hassock with his knees far apart.

- "When your lover draws up one leg, allowing the heel to nestle just behind your knee, and you make love, embracing her forcefully, it is: The Stride." It's best to make sure the man is bending his knees and keeping his back straight for this one. This will give him the strength to handle your weight and the pressure on his knee.

- "If you catch one of her knees firmly in your hand and stand making love with her while her hands explore and caress your body, it is called: The Tripod." Both partners stand for this one. The woman places one foot between the man's two feet and lifts the other foot and leg so that her lover can hold her leg at about his waist in height. Have your lover hold your leg near the ankle or calf to facilitate thrusting.

- "She stands against the wall, lotus-hands on hips, long, lovely fingers reaching to her navel. Cup her foot in your palm and let your free hand caress your angel's limbs. Put your arm around her neck and enjoy her as she leans there at her ease. Vatsyayana and others, who knew the art of love in its great days, called this posture The Palm. If you lean back on a wall and your lover, clinging to your neck, places both her feet in your palms and thus makes love, this is: Two Palms."

• "If you lift your lover by passing your elbows under her knees and gripping her buttocks while she hangs fearfully from your neck, it called: The Knee Elbow." You may get into this position better if you first sit on a bar stool or something high to have him lift you from.

Hints and Tips

The standing positions can be perfect for practice at gaining ejaculation control for the man. Because they require extra physical consciousness, and it's difficult to relax fully, these postures give a man a mindful presence as to his level of excitement. He is in control and is responsible for holding the both of them up. This may cause enough distraction to be helpful.

Talk to your partner! It is better to be vulnerable to your fears and state them to your partner than keeping them to yourself. Things will not get better if you stay quiet about the issues that cause you to hold back during making love.

Pleasure swings are similar in this respect. When the woman is suspended in a swing, and the man is standing, the man is freer to move and manage the stimulus to his *lingam*. He can rest, thrust deeply or more shallowly, slow the pace down, and even practice "Churning Curds" using a swing.

LYING-DOWN POSITIONS

Many of the lying-down positions in the Kama Sutra are rec-
ommended for love partnerships where the woman has a
large type yoni and the man a relatively small size lingam. It
is thought that she can make her yoni tighter by closing her
legs. Most of these lying down positions follow that general
principle.

*The laying-down positions may create more friction on the clito-
ris. More rubbing and squeezing goes on in these positions because
there isn't a lot of traction for thrusting. Rubbing, especially
on the pubic bone, is what works best for clitoral stimulation in
intercourse.*

It is also true, though, that a woman can accommodate
a very large lingam by using these positions to have her thighs
act as part of her yoni. By closing her legs tightly around the
lingam she can "add" to her yoni size by allowing just the tip
of the man's penis to actually enter her while the rest is being
rubbed by her thighs. This keeps the woman from being hurt
and the man thoroughly stimulated.

INVERTED STANDING POSITIONS

Positions such as the Wheelbarrow are healthy for the glandu-
lar system and are fun to try if you are careful. You'll need to be
fairly physically fit to try these positions. Strong arms and legs
are a must. Find ways to move into these positions as a natural
adaptation from other, less strenuous ones.

The Wheelbarrow

In the Wheelbarrow Position the woman is on her hands only and has her head on the floor, a pillow, or free from support. The man is standing. He supports her by holding her legs and feet in the air while he enters her. Generally, the woman's legs would be at about his hip's height, much like a wheelbarrow's handles might be.

This position is erotic to the man as he has a birds-eye view of gorgeous buttocks and the pelvic freedom to thrust effortlessly. A variation on this theme is to have the woman resting on a hassock or footstool so that she is a little higher up in relationship to her partner. To get into this position more easily, you can start by using the "Congress of the Cow" ("When a woman stands on her hands and feet like a quadruped, and her lover mounts her like a bull, it is called: the Congress of the Cow.") The man can then pick up one or two of the woman's feet and lift her legs to hold them. There are shoulder supports for inversion postures in yoga that may add an interesting dimension to this position too.

The Inverted Crow

The classic "69" oral-sex position is the basis for this standing position variation. It may not be too difficult for a woman who is relatively small to try this position. She can hook her legs over the man's shoulders to help hold herself in position and use her hands on his knees for additional support. Some of the love furniture that is on the market might be useful for her to rest her head on in this position.

CHAPTER 15

the lover's fit

*a*h, the dance of the sexes. When it works, it works well, but you can't always take this for granted, especially in a new relationship. How do you know that you will be compatible? What do you do if you're not? When you've got the mix of emotions, character, body dimensions, experience, and even cultural and religious beliefs, how do you understand and work with what the two of you bring to the union?

THE TEMPERAMENTS OF MEN AND WOMEN

The ancient Taoist philosophers from China taught that a woman's energy comes from the heavens and moves down, through her body, and that a man's energy moves from the earth and up, through his body. This is a veiled way of saying that women want love and heart connection first, and then they will warm up to the idea of sexual activity. The men, on the other hand, want sexual activity first, and then they will warm up to love and heart connection. This single idea provides a summation for what many couples feel they experience about each other's temperaments in sexual partnerships.

Yin and Yang

The sexual war of the sexes; she needs heart connection before she wants to have sexual connection, whereas he needs sex before he wants to have heart connection. You have seen the symbol of the yin/yang circle with the light and the dark intersecting halves that curl around each other. This symbol is a representation of both the masculine energy (yang energy) and the feminine energy (yin energy). In the big picture, the symbol also represents the world or the individual and the balance that might be sought in those realms too.

Understanding that these oppositions exist in each of us and that the world is constructed this way helps to calm fears and move us forward in finding new ways to love. Learning new positions is one of the best ways to deconstruct the anomaly of opposites. Your choice of positions can have a influence on your yin/yang relationship.

Living in this world you encounter sadness, violence, hurt, and what modern psychologists call the "shadow." It is present in each of our individual lives. You have your parts that you feel safer hiding from a person close to you, and on the other hand you have the great parts that you are proud of and want to share. This is called the "light" and can be seen in people everywhere when they are generous, compassionate, and loving toward others around them.

Proceeding in the Face of Opposites

Yin is Taoist for the feminine or receptive principle. Yang is the male or active principle. The position you choose, and its appropriateness for your particular needs, can make the difference in whether you experience a female-male "energy dance" or a "war of the sexes." When a woman opens up her sexual repertoire to include trying positions where she is on top and in control, she becomes the "male" principle, or the yang one in the sex act at that moment. This empowers her, and can give her a growing confidence in taking a more sexually active role.

When the male is on the bottom, he can move into his more yin, or feminine, side. This takes the heat off, so to speak. He can relax. He doesn't have to be in charge and perform. The simple act of trying a new position can often be transformative for a relationship.

Yin/Yang in Everyday Life

Moving these principles forward to extend into our everyday actions can be challenging for some people. The woman who refuses to check her own car's oil, help plant the family garden, drive the car while going somewhere with her man, or explore understanding of the household plumbing is not a very integrated person. If she is caught up in how she looks at all times and portrays herself as the helpless, incapable feminine woman, she will draw to her a man who embodies her opposite. She will then complain bitterly that he doesn't listen, can't "feel," and is insensitive. They are holding opposite poles for each other and neither of them will have an easy time breaking the co-dependence of the relationship.

Without having the stressful push to become a "super woman," learn to say yes to a variety of experiences and responsibilities in life. Look to see if something you are being asked to do is an opportunity to expand who you are in ways that may be a little challenging.

The male force men must surmount is the one to be the leader, the "doer," the macho man, and the action figure. The key, for instance, in learning to have multiple orgasmic peaks is to completely relax while in high states of arousal. This is a very "yin" or feminine energy. Being vulnerable to the idea of not knowing everything or having all the answers is a valuable position to be in. Men should practice letting their intuition lead sometimes. This is a wonderful lesson in expanding a more "feminine" perspective.

THE KINDS OF PHYSICAL UNIONS

The Kama Sutra divides men and women into several distinctive categories depending on the size of the genitals, the nature of the desire of the individual, their timing, and the shape of their genitals. As you can imagine it gets to be quite a science to determine exactly who you are in this milieu of combinations. These categories and combinations may help you if you are in the extreme of either end of the spectrum. Otherwise, it may be wise to read them purely for the erotic knowledge.

Genital Categories

Yoni and *lingam* sizes are said to be of three kinds with a total of nine combinations possible for intercourse. Man is divided into three classes: the Hare Man, the Bull Man, and the Horse Man, according to the size of his *lingam*. Woman also, according to the depth of her *yoni*, is either a female deer, a mare, or a female elephant:

- The Hare Man is a lively individual with a slight body type and a gentle manner. His lingam is considered to be of the small variety and measures about six finger widths in length, which is equivalent to about 4 inches.

- The Bull Man has a sturdy body and holds himself with esteem. He is considered of a medium size and his temperament is hearty and energetic. When erect, he measures about eight finger widths, or 5½ inches.

- The Stallion, or Horse Man, is the largest of the three. He is said to be tall and muscular and has a sense of adventurism and daring. He measures twelve finger widths, which equals about 8 inches.

- The Deer Woman is the smallest of the types of women. She's of slight build and gentle, and it is said that her secretions smell like a new lotus blossom opening. Her *yoni* is narrow and not very deep, thus she is best pared with the Hare Man.

- The Mare Woman has a medium size *yoni*. She is said to be sturdy in body, and conducts life with a flare. Her personality is positive and sensuous. She is best suited to partner with a Bull Man, and her vulva area is full and generous.

- The Elephant Woman is large boned and often has a taller than average body. She is affable and agreeable and can have a rather ruddy complexion. She is best partnered with a Horse Man as he can bring her deep *yoni* the most pleasure.

Expanding Ancient Beliefs

Though these categories are rather simplistic, they do point out that humans can vary tremendously in their features. It is more obvious that men differ in the size of their genitals than women, as their genitals are mostly hidden. The largest percentage of men and women fall into the center category, though, with exceptions on either side.

In a survey of 2,400 people on the Tantra.com Web site, less than 29 percent said they liked their body size and shape. Cultural images of skinny models and big muscles tend to lead us astray in understanding that our bodies work well for us when we put aside our self-talk and come fully to the present moment in our sexual activities.

Though it seems rational and wise advice to pick a partner that fits your size, you can't tell your mind who to fall in love with. There will always be those lovers who may not have the perfect fit. With creative attention to the variety of positions that can be used to shape your experience there need not be any "low" unions, as Vatsyayana called the imperfect fit.

164

The G-spot is only about 1½ inches inside of the yoni. If both partners are in good health and the woman has kept her PC or vaginal muscles in strong shape, the size of the partner's genitals isn't really of concern. A variety of great sexual positions can create the best connections when both the man and woman understand their bodies and know the very best ways to guarantee a pleasurable experience.

Lingam *Shapes*

In addition to size, ancient texts examine the distinct shapes of a man's *lingam*. These shapes have nothing to do with size. Again, three categories are cited:

- A penis with the head and shaft of the same dimensions in width.
- A penis with the shaft thicker than the head.
- A penis with the head thicker around than the shaft.

The penis with the head thicker around than the shaft is said to be the best shape for friction to the G-spot in the woman, hence the most pleasure. The frenulum catches on the G-spot with every stroke out and puts a maximum amount of pressure in this area. Positions in which the woman puts her legs back against her body and in high positions on her partner's shoulders can create the same pressure and friction. Approximately 80 percent of men have penises that are "average" size: this means between 5 and 7 inches in length with the most common being 6 to 6½ inches. Girth is commonly between 4½ and 5½ inches.

THE KINDS OF EMOTIONAL UNIONS

The scholars who wrote the sutras were also interested in the duration in timing and the passion that each individual might bring to a sexual encounter. They understood that there are many types of people – some more passionate than others, others more intense or thinking types. Calm, nervous, or aggressive – there are matches for everyone and lovemaking styles to suit all types.

"A man is considered to have small passion when he has little desire for union with a woman, who does not exert himself much at the time, and whose flow is scanty. He also evades the woman's teeth marks. When a man has some force of passion, he belongs to the second class and if his passion is very strong, he qualifies for the third, intense class". "Similarly, women are reckoned to have the three varying degrees of passion, and nine different combinations, exactly like those based on dimensions."

Timing Temperaments

Timing in sexual activity means that one man may take longer to get aroused than another man – as it is with women. There is a misconception that men are always ready for sex. This isn't true. In addition, both men and women go through periods when they have a fluctuation of sexual desire. Job stress, family obligations, and life pressures can put an undue amount of constraint on the most balanced of people causing their passionate pursuits to wane. This is natural and to be expected.

"Again, there are three types of men and women according to their individual passions – short timed, medium timed, and long timed, and there are nine combinations of possible unions, as before." There is disagreement though when the discussion turns to the pleasure derived from sexual activity. "The woman does not discharge the same way as the man. While the man, by merely uniting with the woman, is able to fulfill his passion, the woman takes pleasure in the consciousness of desire and this gives her the kind of pleasure that is totally different from the man's."

The passage implies that women have a kind of spiritual orgasm but not a real, physical one. This is obviously not true and in other areas of the Kama Sutra it is countered with the idea that women do "emit" like men and, in fact, do orgasm distinctly. It further suggests that women do not like men who are of the short-timed variety because they do not feel satisfied when making love to them. They ejaculate too early.

Learn Your Sexual Nature

Modern doctors and psychologists understand that men and women cover the full spectrum along the lines of timing. If partners are patient and are both willing to learn more about their own partner's needs and issues, as well as their own, there are no reasons why this should be an issue with lovers.

Sometimes psychological, organic, or physical issues can keep men and women from being orgasmic at all or ejaculating too fast. See your doctor if these kinds of things are causing problems in your life. Do learn new things about your own sexual nature by applying and trying these new things. Relax, let go, and expand your sexual and sensual attitudes.

Practice keeping your eyes soft and open during the many different situations you encounter in your day. If you can do it during sex, you will be a lot more comfortable with this practice in the rest of the situations you find yourself in.

BODY CHARACTERISTICS AND GENITAL SIZE

The Chinese Taoists developed involved theories about body parts and even posture as it might pertain to genital size and sexual temperament. These theories developed over thousands of years and so may be considered at least somewhat accurate. Though none of us would go around searching the thumb shape or eye structure in order to find a prospective mate, it's an interesting study in possibilities.

Marriage Partners in Ancient Times

In the days when parents and matchmakers found marriage partners for their children, it was important to choose robust and good sexual matches. People were very concerned with continuing their lineages, producing grandchildren, and honoring their ancestors. Matches were made when the two to be married were very young, and so facial and body structure, as well as foot and hand structure, became important factors in choosing partners.

Facial Characteristics

Some of the interesting conclusions include eye structure patterns that can indicate certain types of people. People with large eyes tend to be great lovers. Small eyes indicate a rational, straight thinking personality type. Men with large eyes are expert lovers, whereas women with large eyes are more open and willing. Most cultures believe that the eyes are the windows to the soul. That is why it is important to leave a soft light on while making love and to practice keeping your eyes open during sexual activity. Witnessing your lover and having him or her witness you creates an intimate bubble that surrounds the couple and keeps them completely connected.

What is your sexual profile? Look at these categories and rate yourself by making a simple list of the qualities that you see in yourself. If you are partnered, ask your lover to do the same. If you see some areas where you believe you may not quite mesh, list some creative ideas to help you expand your lovemaking in those areas.

The Taoists believed that abundant facial and body hair means that you have a deep sexual appetite. Thick eyebrows equal thick pubic hair, which was very desirable. Full, long eyebrows on a man indicate a long, robust penis.

Full, fleshy ear lobes and large ears predict a strong sexual appetite. Long noses in men indicate long, strong *lingams*. Small, flat noses in women indicate a warm personality and a short, wide vaginal canal. If the nose of the woman is long it predicts a sexually aggressive woman with an abundance of energy.

Hand Characteristics

The Taoists constructed a detailed analysis of the structure of the hands and fingers for predicting the size of men and women's genitals. They believed that long, straight fingers, especially the first finger, indicated a long penis. In contrast, short, stocky fingers indicated a thick penis. A thumb that is narrow at the base where it meets the hand but wide at the tip means that this man possesses a penis with a head that is larger than the shaft. This is a good sign for a great lover.

Women with straight fingers have a wide vaginal opening and a wide interior vagina. If their thumbs are narrow at the base near the hand and wide at the tip, then the entrance to the vagina is narrow and the interior is wide. Short fingers indicate a short, narrow vaginal canal.

CREATING THE PERFECT FIT

Sometimes a couple won't have the best possible fit with their body parts for sex. A woman might have a large vagina, while her partner has a smaller penis. Other men might envy a man with a large penis, but he will often complain that lovers leave him because he hurts them.

By exploring techniques that expand intercourse and nonintercourse stimulation, and by studying ancient books such as the Kama Sutra, you can easily overcome these obstacles.

Experiment with New Positions

Any couple experiencing these and other "fit" problems should experiment with new positions to get the best out of their lovemaking. Positions that hurt the woman or don't allow her to move her hips and adjust her body to her partner's are going to contribute to an uncomfortable sexual experience. If the woman or man can't communicate problems like this, the couple may begin to shy away from sexual activity.

This can be the beginning of a downhill spiral in the relationship. The couple may never come out of it, all because neither person could say that he or she wasn't comfortable with the way their sexual experiences were going. Exploring new positions can help.

The vagina will, in most cases, expand or tighten to fit the penis. Foreplay and turn-ons for the woman make a tremendous amount of difference. It's a rare case that the fit just won't work at all.

POSITIONS FOR LARGE COUPLES

Your willingness to remain supple in your body and to maintain a fun attitude goes a long way in creating new experiences for you as partners. Your body is your temple, so don't get stopped by issues such as size and shape. Each position can be played with, experimented with, added to, and explored by any size couple, but these suggestions work well for larger couples.

The positions that might best suit you are the rear entry, modified Yab-Yum, woman on top, and a kind of scissors form. One key is to have a lot of varied-sized pillows around the bed so that you are perfectly comfortable with some of these modifications. You may even want to try a love-swing to create a feeling of weightlessness.

Rear-Entry Positions

Rear-entry positions are unique in that the woman is facing away from her partner. This keeps your tummies from competing for space. The woman can either be on all four hands and knees with the man behind, or she can be in this same position but the man is standing. This gives both of you maximum leeway to move around. This is also an excellent G-spot position and, and in general, standing increases the strength of the man's erection. I highly suggest a hand mirror for you to hold so that the two of you can eye gaze while making love.

Modified Yab-Yum Position

The Modified Yab-Yum Position is when the man sits on a fairly firm surface with his legs out and slightly apart. His partner would sit on him with a firm pillow under her buttocks. She can lean back slightly against a wall or headboard as a variation. This would increase the friction on her G-spot.

Experiment, experiment, experiment – try new positions, use pillows and love furniture, create scenarios that appeal to your imaginations, tease and titillate each other, and get away to other locations. In other words – play at sex! Child-like innocence can serve you well in the bedroom.

Woman Superior Positions

In the woman-superior positions, if you stay upright and don't lean toward your partner too much, your tummies won't get in the way and, again, this is a great G-spot position. If it is appropriate, hang a bar or rod from the ceiling that the woman can hold on to during lovemaking to lift herself up and down with. This creates easier thrusting and it's fun and a exciting to consider. You can take it down when not in use.

The Twinning Branches

The Twinning Branches is an easy position that can be relaxing, too. It is easiest to describe by using your hands to first create the concept with. Open up the fingers on both of your hands, make the "scissors" shape with your first and second fingers on each hand, and put them together to "cut" each other. The resulting shape would be the position that the two of you would assume. This position is comfortable and restful and is easily adjusted to get the best fit for both of you.

POSITIONS FOR MISMATCHED COUPLES

Many people are involved in relationships where one of the members is very much taller than the other. This is usually the man but not always. Some sexual positions just won't work very well for these couples because they can't get near enough to each other. According to the Taoists, the tall man may also have quite big genitals, while the woman may have smaller than average depth to her *yoni*.

Again, pillows and love furniture can be helpful to these couples. Beanbag chairs, hassocks, love swings, stuffed sofa arms, and large pillows can add both the dimension of adventure and they can help with the bodily discrepancies. If you are athletically inclined, try some of the standing postures or positions detailed in Chapter 14.

All women, whether of the Deer type, the Mare type, or the Elephant type, should be practicing their PC muscle or Kegel exercises. You will increase your sexual desire, your focus, your orgasmic potential, and you will pleasure yourself and your partner more effectively.

Spoon positions work well for couples where his *lingam* is large and she has a hard time accommodating its full length. By holding her legs close together during intercourse the woman can add friction to her partner's penis and also protect herself from too deep of thrusting. This is important because the G-spot is only a little ways into the woman so for her to be sexually aroused he may need to do some thrusting patterns with some shallow thrusts and then some deeper thrusts.

When a couple is partnered where the woman has a generous *yoni* and the man may be more of the Hare-type man or even the Bull-type man, the couple should use positions that allow the woman to open her legs very freely. She should also try to stay limber enough to be able to put her legs up on her partner's shoulders to increase the angle of penetration. This causes the penis to enter the vagina at a more oblique angle. This adds much more friction to the encounter.

orgasm mastery

*T*he Kama Sutra illustrates many different positions, ways of being partnered, the arts one should study, and a myriad of other prescriptions for a good sex life, but it doesn't teach exactly how to experience orgasm. It is particularly remiss when it comes to women. Time and focus is needed for orgasm mastery, but the knowledge of the genitals and each individual's sexual response curve is especially important.

ORGASM VARIETY

The understanding and care that a woman might require to reach the orgasmic state may not have been understood by some men in the Kama Sutra's culture. When you read the passage below, it appears that this particular scholar was unaware of what an orgasm was like in women. It actually appears as though the women might not have known, either, or at least, didn't express themselves.

Females do not emit as males do. The males simply remove their desire, while the females, from their consciousness of desire, feel a certain kind of pleasure, which gives them satisfaction, but it is impossible for them to tell you what kind of pleasure they feel. The fact from which this becomes evident is, that males, when engaged in coition, cease of themselves after emission, and are satisfied, but it is not so with females. – Auddalika, an ancient scholar, in response to a passage in Part 3, Chapter 1 of the Kama Sutra

This passage proves that women are either multiorgasmic and actually crave repeat orgasms or, as is the case with some women, don't know what orgasm is. Yes, pleasure is felt, but the actual release to the point of vaginal and uterine contractions isn't experienced. When they finally have a true orgasm, the gates are opened for the recognition of the actual experience.

Orgasms can feel brief, expansive, deep, short, extended, mild, earthshaking, odd, and any other variety of adjectives you might want to prescribe to them. Strong ones can come when you least expect them, or when you do expect, they can be "blips." Unless you are well trained in the matters of love, you just never know what you are going to get.

Orgasm, in both men and women, varies from person to person and from moment to moment. The same person might recognize that he or she has a variety of experiences depending on mood, situation, timing, place, stress, and more. The more experience and expansive understanding that you have, the more consistent your pleasure will be.

THE CLITORAL ORGASM

Long heralded as "the only avenue to female orgasm," the clitoris has always been known as the woman's pleasure center. The clitoris has the largest bundle of nerve endings of any organ in the body, male or female. It stays active from birth to death, and is as much a source of pleasure as it is frustration.

Know Thyself

The clitoris is located on the outside of the woman's body toward the top of her vulva – the opening to her vagina. The same tissue that makes up the sides of the vulva and the labia covers the clitoris with a hood of skin. The hood extends over the clitoris and generally covers it to protect it from overstimulation.

In the past, many young women have been encouraged not to touch themselves, or explore their genital area. They may have been shamed, discouraged, and even threatened by an authority figure in their life. As a result, these women didn't give themselves permission to self-pleasure or at least explore their "Sacred Garden" until later in life.

Many women still don't feel comfortable touching themselves, let alone receiving the full pleasure that is their birthright. No wonder that they feel struggle or at least frustration when it comes to orgasmic pleasure. But you must know what pleases you (pressure, stroke, etc.) and how to facilitate an orgasm in yourself.

Building a Wave of Pleasure

When the clitoris is stimulated, it begins to fill with a surge of blood, much like the penis. The spongy material around the nerve bundle fills and causes the clitoris to actually become erect. As this happens, the clitoris enlarges slightly, and you begin to be more aroused. If you are getting the kind of stimulus you like, you should continue the build of excitement toward an orgasm.

However, often at the point of around eight – on an arousal scale of one to ten – the woman will have a variety of experiences that will prevent her from continuing the climb toward orgasm. She may tense her body excessively, she may stop breathing altogether, or she may worry that she's taking too long – both physical and mental bad habits may creep into her experience to put a damper on her pleasure.

Becoming conscious of the minute details of your orgasmic potential seems like a selfish thing, but the opposite is true. When you become good at managing and receiving your own pleasure, you will want sex much more. It will be satisfying and rejuvenating. This is a journey with a goal for both of you to travel.

Learning to relax and deep breathe into the belly will help tremendously. Focusing your mind on your pleasure sensations is a wonderful way to actually learn a kind of meditation technique. Learning to break down the barriers that prevent you from communicating what you need to your partner will greatly enhance both of your experiences.

This focused attention to yourself will also allow you to develop a kind of wave of sensations that you can trust and ride all the way to orgasm. There may be hills and valleys but there are no ravines to fall into. As you master this wave you will get better at knowing your body's responses and how to respond to them.

Clitoral Advice

In erotic love manuals of the East, including the Kama Sutra, the hand position that is often referred to for stimulating the woman's clitoris is called *Angulirata*. It is described as using the first three fingers on the hand together to form a kind of an elephant's trunk shape. Put your fingers together such that if you look down at the three fingertips of your fingers you'll notice that they form a triangle. Your middle finger is positioned on top of the two other fingers that are close together but not quite touching.

By forming the fingers in this configuration it is possible to anchor the clitoral shaft and stimulate the head and tip of the clitoris. The clitoris' nerve bundle can be illusive and a bit wiggly. By anchoring the shaft, you can keep it stationary, and massage and stimulate it appropriately. The two outside fingers anchor it and the middle finger stimulates.

THE G-SPOT AND VAGINAL ORGASM

According to most books on sex, there are two places in a woman's body that (when stimulated) can lead to an orgasm. The first is called the G-spot, but where it is and what it feels like are questions many women, and men, find unanswered. The second area is found in the vagina, back near the cervix opening and on top. It is a misconception that the vagina is a sensitive organ. It doesn't actually have many nerve endings, and other than the entrance – which has some sensitivity – these two areas are what you have to work with.

Location

Here's a little exercise: Place the tip of your tongue at the back of your front teeth, just touching the teeth. Move your tongue very slowly backward until you feel the ridge area that is rough and bumpy. As you slip past that area, you'll notice that the roof of your mouth begins to feel slick and smooth. You've gone too far.

Go back, with the very tip of your tongue, and find the place where these two meet. Just as the rough area ends, hold the tip there for a minute and place your conscious mind there too. That place is exactly analogous to the area where the G-spot is in your *yoni*. The *yoni* is even shaped similarly to your upper palate. Try doing this same exercise with your thumb or finger in your mouth. Have your partner do it too, in his mouth.

The G-spot is located right behind the pubic bone, just past the rough and ridge-like area on top of the vagina. It isn't very far in, about 1½ inches in most women and it is more of an area than a spot. It may burn, hurt a little, feel intense, feel great, or even tickle when you first realize it is there.

What to Do with It

If you think that you have located something in this area that feels a little different, great. Now, get turned on. Stimulate your clitoris, with or without a partner, to the point of about an eight on the Richter scale. You will have an easier time actually finding your G-spot if you are turned on.

If you are stimulating yourself, a good position is to be on your knees so that you can reach your spot. Lying on your back will make it more difficult. Use the middle finger of your dominant hand to feel the area of the G-spot. Press quite firmly – you will be surprised how much pressure it takes. Use a come-hither motion of your finger to stroke the area.

If your partner is there with you, it is best to lie down with your legs bent at the knees and supported by pillows on either side. Your partner can sit to one side of you so that his dominant hand is free to enter your *yoni*. Partners, please pay very close attention to your lover. This is a vulnerable activity, especially if you are new to it. Keep eye contact with your lover.

Once inside, try moving your finger slowly from side to side, like a windshield wiper. Then try the come-hither stroke. The Giver can ask for feedback, and the Receiver should give quality feedback to the lover. Tell your partner what feels good and what doesn't. Tell what sensations you are having and any emotions that might be welling up.

A survey by Carol Rinkleib Ellison in her book **Women's Sexualities** *found that 38 percent of 2,600 women studied had not once had an orgasm during intercourse. If this is you, you are not alone.*

Partners can remind each other to deep breathe during this exploration. Even the Giver forgets to breathe sometimes. Relax and don't do too much exploration the first time. Make a commitment to try again soon and that time you can go a little longer. Build up to more intense pressure and speed slowly. Trust that you will discover the deep pleasure of this area.

Intercourse and the G-spot

As you practice exploring this area with your fingers (and your lover's fingers), hold the image of it in your mind. You can do this a lot easier if you are practicing your PC muscle exercises. Strong vaginal muscles help you focus your attention on different areas of your vagina. Visualize your G-spot with your mind.

During intercourse, have your partner do some shallow thrusting so that the head of his lingam just brushes the vaginal lips and the inside of your *yoni*. The stroke on the way out is often the most effective. Try this in positions in which the woman has her legs up high, say on her lover's shoulders. The angle of penetration will be conducive to G-spot stimulation. Try different positions to see which seem best for you.

FEMALE EJACULATION

Yes, it's true, women ejaculate. It typically doesn't come in cups but in about the same amount that a man's ejaculate comes in. It can pulse out, squirt out, dribble out, or come in little pulses. The women who recognize that they ejaculate tend to have strong vaginal muscles, good deep-breathing techniques, and often make deep sounds when they are in ecstasy.

Many women have been embarrassed that they "wet the bed" during sex and have done everything in their power to try to prevent it from occurring. We now know that women ejaculate and it has become something that women want to do. Don't push yourself to learn to ejaculate, though. It can be freeing, but it doesn't necessarily add to the orgasmic experience.

During G-spot play, you may want to try really opening up your vocal cords and letting out deep, resonate sounds and moans from your mouth. Play with the sounds freely to see what happens. Try it some time when the kids aren't home. Don't worry too much about the neighbors.

Your partner isn't responsible for your orgasmic pleasure — you are. It is your responsibility to know what you need and to ask for it appropriately. Don't blame your lover if you are not getting the proper stimulation that you need to have orgasm pleasure.

Be prepared with a thick towel and a willing spirit. You will feel the urge to pee but that is just your urethra being stimulated near the entrance of your vagina. It doesn't mean you are going to urinate. Sometimes a little pee is pushed out from the bladder during ejaculation so before trying this, go to the bathroom and make sure you have emptied your bladder.

THE MALE ORGASM

Women think that men just seem to come equipped with all the right gear and responses to have orgasms easily and effortlessly. Because their parts are so external, most men have had a long history of self-loving activities. They know what brings them pleasure and are practiced at receiving it. The down side is they can be a little too good at it.

Myth has it that men are always ready for sex. Their penises gets hard at the drop of a hat and they can have orgasms with no problems – all the time. But men know better. Many obstacles can get in the way with orgasm and ejaculation. Yet most men enjoy the pleasures that orgasmic release brings with only a few off-times throughout the years of their lives.

Early Training

Young men tend to masturbate, or self-pleasure, a lot more than young girls. Usually, young men train themselves to ejaculate quickly. This happens because of guilty feelings or the thought that they might get caught. Many Western societies tend to frown upon masturbation in both sexes. As they get older, young men aren't taught that there are other ways to manage their sexual energy and the orgasmic reflex.

Being a Great Lover

Most men want to be great at loving. Sex is important to them, and they have a vested interest in being considered good at it. By the time a man reaches his childbearing years, he often begins to slow his timing down to accommodate his lover. He'll learn that it's all right to take his time and really enjoy the sensations of sexual and sensual touch.

Smoking cigarettes and drinking excessive amounts of alcohol are the number one killers of erections. Because the penis is far from the heart, it takes extra work for the blood to get there. These activities clog the arteries that supply the necessary blood flow to the penis.

Lovers and partners tend to go on the journey together to learn and expand what they know about sex. This deepening can lead to extraordinary experiences that will reinforce the commitment to excel at sex and the intimate connection it brings. This is what brought ancient scholars, like Vatsyayana, to write books on the subject. Knowledge and the subtleties that come with experience can add up to unimaginable pleasure.

Inhibitors to Good Sex

As both men and women get older, their blood flow gets more sluggish because the arteries begin to narrow. The blood flow to the penis decreases and becomes sluggish, also. At the same time, the veins that carry the blood back out of the penis begin to lose their elasticity and leak blood back out at the most inappropriate times.

It's important to keep having sex. The sex act counteracts the actions of normal aging. "Use it or lose it" is an active principle here. Men who practice even a marginal amount of ejaculation control have stronger, longer erections, too.

The two biggest complaints men have about their sex lives are that they think their penis is too small and that they ejaculate too fast. Penis size has very little to do with a good lover if he knows what he is doing. Learning ejaculation mastery is fun and pretty easy for most men to accomplish in a very short time!

Both men and women should take their vitamins and supplements. Try L-Arginine, as it opens arteries and increases blood flow. If you are on prescription medications that already do this, then try a topical cream that has the same effect. There are also creams that can have a very similar effect to Viagra for many men. The same creams are also available for women. However, make sure they have L-Arginine in them.

SIMULTANEOUS ORGASMS

Simultaneous orgasms sometimes happen to couples that spend a long time making love and are very attentive to each other. Having an orgasm at the same time as your partner is an ideal that is hard to count on achieving. The longer the man lasts and the more tuned in the woman is to her orgasmic response level, the more possible this elusive act is.

The deep knowing that occurs in long-time partnerships and with lovers who are very attuned to their partner's rhythms can help lead to the possibility of mutual orgasms. Staying aware of your lover's breath patterns, response levels, subtle movements, and reflexes will keep you in sync with each other's timing. The man who can last the time it takes for his lover to reach orgasm can begin anticipating her responses and then allow himself to reach the same climactic regions with her. This takes training and time to be able to count on it, some of the time. It is never a sure thing, but two people committed to training their responses levels to parallel the other's can achieve this level of intimacy.

Achieving mastery at simultaneous orgasms is the beginning of the place that the master's called "Performing Sexual Magic." This art begins the world of the possibilities of union that borders on prayer. It is considered "High Sex" and is the ultimate jumping off point for Tantric sex and a union so divine that the lovers become lost or blended as if they are but one being or energy.

CHAPTER 17

aphrodisiacs, sex aids and the occult

*T*hroughout history, human beings have sought to enhance the sexual experience through eating, smoking, pleasure devices and toys, and stimulation of the imagination. The Kama Sutra combines Ayurvedic principles, folk medicines, artificial phalli, and even piercing to create a treasure chest of erotic possibilities. As you will see from the compilation of sex aids in this chapter, almost anything can add to your pleasure if your mind associates it with sex.

WHAT IS AN APHRODISIAC?

An aphrodisiac is typically considered to be any substance that you ingest or activity you take part in to enhance pleasure. The list of possible aphrodisiacs is probably endless, since every person has had different early life experiences associating certain foods, odors, or environments with sex.

Some of the well-publicized aphrodisiacs in ancient times were rhinoceros horn, elk antler, and powdered sea horse. Asian people have used these substances for thousands of years to produce heightened sexual response. There is little evidence that these substances actually work, however, and serious damage is being done to the environment today because of these ancient beliefs.

Things that mimic the shape of the phallus or the vulva have always been considered aphrodisiacs. Cucumbers, eggplants, orchids, bananas, and oysters all have a reputation. Spanish fly, soma from the ancient Asian cultures, and many plants including the datura plant have had long reputations for their erotic powers.

What other things turn you on? Make a short list of items that increase your desire and stimulate your libido. Share this list with your lover and ask him to do the same. Notice the things that are the same and the ones that are different.

Also, a good deal of evidence exists associating some everyday items with enhanced sexual interest or arousal. These things include erotic art, certain genital-like flowers, a sensual setting, watching a sexual video, reading erotic literature, compassion, vulnerability, looking at erotic books, deep breathing and relaxation, talking about sex, shared physical exercise, teasing and touch, words of love, certain smells and foods, and many herbs and extracts.

LOVE POTIONS FROM THE KAMA SUTRA

Love potions and aphrodisiacs have existed since the beginning of human consciousness. Desire and its conquest seem to be innate properties of human beings. In an established culture such as that of India's, the centuries of experimentation have given a few very juicy recipes for increasing potency and stamina, drawing a desired lover to you, and increasing arousal and sexual desire.

To Enslave a Lover

These recipes are folk remedies that were used in ancient times to enslave a lover. More subtle recipes are used today. Wouldn't you rather drink a little champagne and eat oysters than dust your lover's penis with powdered peacock bone? These things may work, though. What do you think?

- "Leaves caught as they fall from trees and powdered with peacock-bone and fragments of a corpse's winding-sheet will, when dusted lightly on the penis, bewitch any woman living."
- "If you crush milky chunks of cactus with sulphur and realgar, dry the mixture seven times, powder it, add honey, and apply it to your penis, you'll satisfy the most demanding lover."
- "And if, to these powerful ingredients, you add monkey's dung, grind them together and sprinkle the powder on your unsuspecting lover's head, she will be your devoted slave for life."

To Increase Potency

Today you can consider some of the more conventional methods of increasing potency and wellbeing, including healthy living, vitamins, and supplements. Even Viagra and the new pharmaceuticals that are coming to the marketplace might be a better source than sparrow eggs or monkey dung!

- "If ghee, honey, sugar, and licorice in equal quantities, the juice of the fennel plant, and milk are mixed together, this nectar-like composition is said to be holy, and provocative of sexual vigor, a preserver of life, and sweet to the taste."
- "Anoint your penis, before lovemaking, with honey into which you have powdered black pepper, long pepper and datura – you will completely satisfy your woman."
- "Honey-sweetened milk in which the testicles of a ram or a goat have been simmered has the effect, when drunk, of making a man as powerful as a bull."
- "Pumpkin seeds ground with almonds and sugarcane root, or with cowhage root and strips of bamboo, and stirred into honeyed milk, have the same arousing effect."
- "The sages say that wheat-flour cakes baked with honey and sugar and sprinkled with the powdered seeds of pumpkin and cowhage give one strength for a thousand women."
- "The yolk of a single sparrow's egg stirred into rice pudding that has been thickened with cream, wild-

honey and 'ghee' (clarified butter) has the same invigorating effect."

To Boost the Potential of the Penis

The use of wasps and other stinging insects to increase the girth and length of the *lingam* was well known in ancient India. But today, this seems a wild and risky technique. Undoubtedly this practice was done under the direction of a qualified physician, or Ayurvedic practitioner.

- "Take shuka hairs – the shuka is an insect that lives in trees – mix with oil and rub on the penis for ten nights, take it off then put it on again. When a swelling appears sleep face downwards on a wooden bed, letting one's sex hang through a hole."
- "Thus having obtained the desired result, get rid of the pain with a cooling mixture made of five astringents. This is the way to eliminate the pain caused by the swelling. The swelling caused by a shuka lasts for life."
- "By rubbing it successively with the juice of ashvagandha, or shabara roots, or jala shuka, or brihati, or buffalo butter, or hastikarna, or vajracalli the penis will stay swollen for one month."
- "A man who climaxes too swiftly should arouse his lady by caressing her clitoris with his fingers and flooding the well of her yoni before he enters her."
- "If, during lovemaking, the erection cannot be sustained because the man is old, or simply exhausted

he should use the delicate oral techniques given in an earlier chapter."

The Kama Sutra also goes into great detail about additions the man can have inserted into the foreskin of his *lingam*. A young man would first perforate his *lingam* and then stand in water until the bleeding stopped. He should then make love several times a day for several days so the wound won't heal. He should wash it with various ointments to keep it clean for several weeks. He then proceeds to widen the hole with objects designed for that use.

Many cultures throughout history, and even today, use scarification as a sex aid. Typically, it will involve the man actually splitting portions of his lingam and then inserting objects into it to widen and lengthen his phallus. It can be likened to ear and body-part piercing.

Many types of items are then inserted into the hole. They could be tubular, triangular, pointed, or round. The *lingam* would then adjust over the years to larger and larger items.

Sex Aids
Sex aids were also known in the ancient India, and were employed for certain reasons. Though it doesn't appear that they were used on a regular basis, they were crafted so that a husband and wife could continue amorous intimacy even if the man was not able to manage it on his own. They appear to be

made of quite interesting materials and were best designed to match the *lingam* of the person that they replaced. To increase the size or proportions of his *lingam*, a man also wore artificial phalluses over his own: "The man who is utterly unable to achieve an erection should pleasure his wife/lover with a phallus crafted from materials like gold, silver, copper, iron, ivory or horn. The artificial phallus should be shaped to your natural proportions. It will be more arousing for the lady if the outside is studded with a profusion of large, smooth nodules."

Vatsyayana's Cautions

Throughout the text of the Kama Sutra, Vatsyayana encourages caution and regard for both the man and the woman's preferences. He shows a true voice of sanity when he concludes that, after all of the instruction and the many aphorisms, the couple should always choose for themselves the ideas and practices that suit them best. He encourages citizens to use professionals and to proceed with caution in experimentation of all sorts.

- "A person who wishes to avail of such recipes in the conduct of his love affairs should study them from the Ayurveda and the Tantric texts or otherwise from persons who are acquainted with the practices."
- "Recipes about which the user has the slightest doubt or which cause physical harm, or the killing of some living animal, or which recommend the use of impure ingredients, must be avoided."

- "Only those practices found affective after long trial, approved of by cultured people and blessed by Brahmins and friends, should be resorted to."

- "The ways and means which have been enumerated earlier for the purpose of increasing a man's passion are to be practiced only by those who are absolutely in need of them. They are emphatically forbidden to those who do not need to use them."

- "It is not to be understood that simply because this work mentions certain artifices and expedients, that they are to be used by all and sundry. While the Science is certainly meant to be studied by everybody, the practice of these expedients should be restricted to particular persons who need them."

CHEMICALS OF LOVE

Pheromones are subtle odor-producing substances given off by our bodies unconsciously. We respond physiologically to another person's "scent," even if we cannot consciously smell it. The word *pheromone* is derived from a Greek word meaning "to transfer excitement." Body temperature, skin conductance, heart rate, and blood pressure are just some of the functions that can be affected by our reactions to other people's pheromones.

Pheromones don't have a smell or odor that is discernable, but humans have special detectors in their noses for pheromones. They can be covered up by colognes and perfumes, which mask the effect they have. So before you put on your favorite perfume, consider what you may be giving up.

Research on Pheromones

British researchers have discovered that pheromones affect our attraction to the opposite sex. During a controlled study, women were asked to rate men's pictures according to body shape, face appeal, and other characteristics. During part of the study, the researchers dabbed the rooms with male pheromones. The pictures that the women were asked to evaluate all of a sudden got better ratings, especially the previously "average" men. This was particularly true for women in the midpoint of their monthly cycles and those who did not take oral birth control. Women taking oral contraceptives seem to be less responsive to pheromones.

Other studies have shown that women who live together or in close proximity over a period of time often have the same menstrual cycles. This occurs in households were there are at least several daughters and a mother, college dorms, and among women's sports teams. Pheromones seem to be the regulator causing this synchronizing effect.

Arousal Aids

Some men and women are greatly attracted to the smell of their partner's underarms and hair. Male and female pheromones are excreted from glands in the hair follicles, the underarms, and the groin area. Try burying your nose in your partner's hair the next time you want to become aroused.

Pheromones can be added to your favorite perfume or dabbed on separately. The jury is out on their effectiveness since there haven't been many studies done with manufactured pheromones. They aren't too expensive, so try some out for yourself.

It's said that there is an old custom for men to bury their handkerchiefs under their arms while dancing and then to present the handkerchief to their partner at the end of the dance. Maybe the relatively new advances, like deodorants and scented soaps, have been detrimental to lovers!

SCENTS AND PERFUMES

Scents and perfumes have been used since time immemorial, possibly to mimic pheromone's actions. One of the most popular is musk, which has a smell very close to the male hormone testosterone. The Romans used civet and ambergris as the carriers for lavish perfumes that were erotic in nature.

Vanilla, lavender, and flower essences have been used for thousands of years to add allure to our already present bodily scents. Also, many of the tropical forests in Hawaii were cut down in the eighteenth and nineteenth centuries for the delicate scent of sandalwood. Its wood carries the musky, earthy scent that the finest European fans, for aristocratic women, were made from. This wood never loses its scent, so it served as a perfume when a woman seductively fanned herself.

Picking a Perfume

When choosing a perfume, pick something that isn't overbearing. It should complement the subtle scent of your own skin, hair, and pheromones. Try going without perfume, especially before a night of lovemaking.

Massage and Essential Oils

Some fun additions to a sex-positive bedroom are wet, slippery massage oils. They will help you have a better time when you make love. They're fun to put on your own body and on your lover's body. They teach us to touch with grace and erotic good will. Massage oils are fabulous for soothing massages as well as erotic massages. They should not go into the body, however. Keep them on the outside. Choose a scent that you think you and your lover would like. If it smells erotic, it's the right one for you.

Scents are best when they are natural, essential oils that are created to give the ultimate sensual experience. Popular essential oils used for erotic purposes are vanilla, musk, orange, ylang ylang, rose, cedarwood, geranium, lavender, and lemongrass. Look for blends that turn you on.

You can try making your own, experimenting with different combinations of scents. If you decide to do this, you'll find the leftover essential oils you buy are a wonderful addition to the sensuous baths you and your lover will take.

Simply add a few drops to the next bath for a heightened experience.

Incense

The use of incense has a long history for enhancing the setting in which lovemaking takes place. Again, pick something that is appropriate and not overbearing. You might want to place it in an adjacent room like a bathroom so that the hint of it reaches you rather than having the full strength take over the room you are in. You can also "freshen" a room with incense and then put it out quickly, to give just a hint of the scent.

Asian cultures still use incense to carry their prayers to the gods and goddesses they honor. Temples in China, Singapore, Indonesia, Malaysia, and India are everywhere and the sweet smoke of incense wafts to the streets freely. As the Asians associate incense with prayer, you can associate it with lovemaking. By lighting it and letting the smell gently spread through your house, you can signal a lover that you are thinking about sensual sex.

THE KAMA *FOOD*RA

It's often been said that food is the way to a man's heart. Well, that can have a lot of different implications. Healthy eating is of course the optimum for all of us. Certain foods do have a positive effect on the libido. Indian foods are generally highly spiced and contain spices that are beneficial to our circulatory system and our brain functions.

Oral Courses

If you are planning an evening of lovemaking that includes food, make eating a part of the ritual or ceremony of loving. That way, you can design eating into the sensual evening without it stopping the action. Eating can be a fun addition. You can feed each other. Eat in courses so that eating takes a lengthy time and is spread into courses between the "courses" of love.

Serving things like sushi, light pastas, small skewers of vegetables and fish or a salad with many goodies in it would be perfect before lovemaking. The desert could come later. Maybe you can present dessert on your inner thighs or offer your partner the opportunity to become the platter.

Suggestive Shapes

Many of the folk recipes for increased potency in the Kama Sutra involve foods that are elongated in shape. Try forming foods into shapes that are suggestive or downright sexual, like penises, breasts, and vulvas. These can be little cakes, chocolates, oysters, candies, breads, and main dishes. Your imagination can take you anywhere with this.

Soak dried fruit in wine or liquors to enhance their flavor. Use fresh and dried fruit to dip into sauces that are sweetened and have a yogurt base. Dip fresh fruit into chocolate or butterscotch sauces. Raspberry sauce, whipped cream – even ice cream in moderation – can be used in erotic ways to enhance an evening of love.

Spice Up Your Life

Some spices, seasonings, and foods with certain amino acids are good for raising the "heat." Adding a variety of spices to your food concoctions can have a wonderful effect of heightening arousal. Pumpkin pie spices, licorice, cinnamon, peppermint, curries, coriander, cardamom, lavender, chili peppers, sesame seeds, saffron, nutmeg, pepper, ginger, onions, and garlic are also considered aphrodisiacs by many cultures, and so are asparagus, figs, grapes, almonds, oysters, muscles, caviar, basil, bananas, and mangos.

Anything can be erotic, so create foods that appeal to you and your lover. It's fun creating and discovering new things together, and the time spent attending to the details will be rewarded. You are co-creating a ritual to honor your lovemaking.

Chocolate

One of the active ingredients in chocolate produces phenylethylamine, the chemical that the body manufactures when we fall in love. These chemical messengers speed up the flow of information that travels between our nerve endings. Phenylethylamine is similar in many ways to amphetamine, which dilates the blood vessels and creates energy and focus. It is not by chance that chocolate is highly associated with love.

When the conquistadors invaded Mexico, Montezuma was reported to have drunk up to fifty cups a day of chocolate with chili peppers and spices in it. He had to keep his stamina up to satisfy his many wives. Some women, as their hormonal balance shifts, crave chocolate as an unconscious remedy to lift spirits and provide energy.

Liquor

Used in small amounts, alcohol can enhance the sensual/ sexual experience. It can relax you and ease your inhibitions. In small amounts, it has been cited as an aid in helping men last longer so they don't ejaculate too fast. In larger amounts, it has the opposite effect; "Consuming Dhattura fruit, or its diluted juice, causes intoxication."

Try using it in a ritual way by creating ceremony when you drink it. Sip it during lovemaking. Share a kiss, with a little liquor in your mouth. Let it dribble down your cheeks.

Amaranth flowers were considered particularly reflective of amorous intentions and were auspicious for lovers. Absinthe is a strong liquor that is made from the Amaranth plant. It has been made since the edge of time. It can be deadly in large doses, but it has aphrodisiac properties in small amounts.

Take some liquor into your mouth and then give your partner oral sex while you still have it in your mouth. Throw in the element of surprise. This can add new sensations to both your experiences. It can be licked and sucked off if any gets away from you!

THE OCCULT AND ASTROLOGY

Astrological compatibility was one of the destiny signs that the family considered important to the occasion of marriage. A bride's and groom's families, often before they had ever met each other, would have the charts compared for compatibility, birthing possibilities of the bride, and any potential areas of struggle that the young couple might encounter. Conception and the birth of babies were planned for certain days and periods of time, as well as any ceremony that had auspicious undertones. Magical rites were practiced and astrologists were a part of both kingly courts and village councils. Knowledge of these things was part of the Sixty-Four Arts one could learn.

- "Consulting the omens refers to the signs of destiny, omens deriving from the position of the planets, their conjunctions, influence, and meaning for the boy's future, foretelling a happy destiny for him."
- "Having consulted the omens, the date of the meeting is decided on, then that of the marriage ceremony."
- "The art of framing mystical diagrams, of addressing spells and charms, and binding amulets."
- "If, after smearing his palm with the excreta of the peacock who has partaken of Haritala and Manahshila, a person touches any object, he makes it invisible."
- "The eye of a peacock or a Tarakshu, covered in a golden amulet and worn on the right wrist or upper arm, is efficacious in beautifying oneself. The amulet

must be sealed at an auspicious moment for this to work."

Clearly time, intent, and even place are to be taken into consideration in the pursuit of mystical activities. The use of secret language was common, especially in the pursuit of a lover. And the *Yantras* involved in the religious duties of the citizen's life required artistic abilities, as well as mystical formulas.

becoming an exotic, erotic lover

W hen all is said and done, it's not technique that makes the great lover, it's presence. Feeling passionate, trusting, and loving yourself are very important. When you bring these qualities and great new techniques to the bedroom you have a winning formula for life.

PUTTING IT ALL TOGETHER

Nothing is truer than this statement: "Once the wheel of Love has been set in motion, there is no absolute rule." There is no holding back when passion and desire fuel your actions, but learning some of the things presented in this book will become a part of who you are, and will affect your love life and the way you interact with your lover.

When you encourage personal growth in your life, you are always expanding on and improving upon what has transpired already in your life. The desire to come back to your true self blossoms, and the search for more meaning in life becomes a force that begs notice in your life.

The word Tantra *is a Sanskrit word that means "to weave all of life." Tantra was practiced in ancient India during the time of the Kama Sutra and was the supreme practice of the art of consciousness. It used meditation, yoga, initiation by a guru, secret symbols, and sexuality as the vehicles for life transformation.*

The Fabric of Life

Consciousness involves looking at the subtle aspects of your day-to-day experiences as well as the bigger picture. Life is like a piece of fabric with a warp and a weft – the object is to "weave" the fabric of life into the finest cloth you can imagine. You can "weave" that beautiful fabric of your life with inspiration, love, pleasure, a conscious mind, compassion, and with all the different threads you will bring to your cloth.

The Kama Sutra uses sexuality as a vehicle for transforming what you might normally do without thinking into a more sublime lesson plan for life's fulfillment and enhancement. When you bring consciousness and subtlety to the sexual act, you can make breakthroughs that are profound. More ecstatic energy will be available in your sensual life and in all the other areas of life that you cultivate too.

Honor the Male and the Female

Look for the good in people and in your partner. In a sense, your partner is your "guru." Simply honoring the woman, the female principle, as the universal goddess and the man, the male principle, as the universal god, helps to bring this into your lives. When you see these divine qualities in your partner and yourself, you begin to see these qualities in everyone and everything in your life.

Enjoying Your Own Passion

According to the Kama Sutra, pleasure is one of the three aims of life. The pleasure starts in your own body, so learn to enjoy your own erotic passion, and you'll be happy all your life. Building upon your knowledge of your body's pleasure capacity will bridge the gaps that make you doubt your passion.

Practice what you love passionately. Many people worry that they'll be "too big" and that others won't like them for being that way. Be fully yourself as often as you can. Allow others the same space to show up "big" as well – especially your partner.

The keys are in your breath, health, movement, play, practice, and willingness to expand your sensual self. Notice often what you like about yourself. Breathe deeply into those thoughts, almost like a mini-meditation, so that you'll remember them and have access to them during the times when you don't feel so good.

It's All About You

Many of the exercises outlined in this book do not require you to have a partner. Be creative, and adapt the exercises to your needs by finding a friend to do them with, using a mirror as your partner, or simply imagining the partner you desire. Use your own intuitive self as a springboard for learning, if you aren't currently partnered. Create the possibility of deeper connection, more intimacy, sensuality, and more satisfying sex by expanding your capacity to have pleasure. When you bring a whole individual, yourself, to the world, the world recognizes you. You are empowered and attractive when you have balance and are happy in your life. This attractiveness draws a partner to you. You will call forth a partner and lover that is your equal in interests and life philosophy.

CREATING INTIMACY

Having a deep, intimate connection in your love life is about trusting yourself and your partner. When you give yourself over to vulnerable, open, playful sexuality – that gently pushes your edges and keeps you taking gentle risks – you see how sweet and easy deepening intimacy can be. Doing things together does not necessarily equal intimacy. It's the quality of the time you spend together that counts.

Taking time to talk about goals, problems, work, home, or whatever it is that your life is about is important. Listening attentively and thoughtfully will make your partner feel loved.

Compassion

No one is perfect. You will never find a perfect person so you can stop wasting your time thinking you will. Often, especially as time passes in a love relationship, you begin to get irritated about little things that didn't bother you before. You can struggle with these things or you can ask yourself: "How are these things related to me and how I act or what I do in this relationship?" By doing this creative thinking you can begin to have compassion for your partner and for yourself.

Vulnerability

Being truly vulnerable with your partner can be hard – whether you are a woman or a man. Men aren't very experienced at being vulnerable, and women don't often trust enough to think they will be heard. If this is hard for you, start with easy disclosures – maybe something that hurt you as a child or something that happened to you in your family that made you feel unworthy of attention could be safe to begin with. Whatever it is, speak in "I" statements and speak about your feelings. When you talk about feelings and don't blame others, the listener's heart opens up automatically.

Playfulness

Do more creative things together, even if it feels silly sometimes. Erotic writing, creating love rituals together, designing an erotic evening, breathing together before a sexual encounter, or even practicing PC muscles exercises together are activities that will add tremendously to your love life, as well as to your everyday life. You might want to systematically explore all the different types of positions, have blindfolded touch and pleasuring rituals, or create a situation where you can have sex outside the bedroom. The living room furniture, love-swings, and piles of pillows make what could be an ordinary evening into an extraordinary one.

Don't forget to be playful all the time. Find things to do that engage the two of you to work or create together. Gardening, walks in nature, getting away together, or going to the zoo or a museum are all much more intimate and stimulating than sitting next to each other watching television.

Gently Pushing the Edges

Building trust in a relationship is of the highest importance. If trust is lacking you can't expect either of you to try fun, exciting new things, especially in the bedroom. Vulnerability helps create trust. Trust is necessary to explore adventurous new things together. Remember too that it's good to stay open to trying but if something doesn't work for you, say so to your partner. Discuss openly how you might modify or change the thing to fit both of your needs. Keep pushing those edges, though, to grow and expand with your lover.

COMMUNICATING

Knowing what you want from a lover and being able to ask for it are two important things in any relationship. You need to know what you want, before you can ask for it effectively, though. The next exercise is a wonderful combination of both.

Scenario #1: A couple is in the bedroom, and they've been kissing and warming up to a potential hot evening. Her blouse comes off and he is going for her nipples. He's excited, but his touch is too rough. She's not ready for this. She blurts out, "Ouch, that's too hard." He backs away and they share a moment of very awkward silence. He rolls on his back and turns away – well, you can see where this is going.

If your communication with your partner isn't good don't expect that your sex life will get better. Communication, listening, and telling what hurts you are prerequisites to great sex. When this area of your life is healed your sex life will get much, much better.

Scenario #2: A couple is in the bedroom, and they've been kissing and warming up to a potential lovemaking. Her blouse comes off and he is going for her nipples. He's excited, but his touch is too rough. She's not ready for this. She says, "Oh, I love my nipples fondled. Could you try touching them lightly with just your fingertips?" He immediately tries this because he feels acknowledged and not made wrong. She likes her nipples fondled – she just needs it done with a lighter touch. She says, "Mmm . . . that's perfect."

Communication Structure

By using a simple communication structure to ask for the kind of touch and loving you need, you will also experience learning what you actually want and need. Here is how this simple structure works: *Acknowledge something you like. Ask for a single change. Acknowledge the change.* It's that simple. Look back at the second scenario and see just how the three steps fit in. At step three you may find that you were just experimenting and you didn't care for the change. You could then say, "Gosh, I thought I'd like that but it didn't work as well as I thought it might." You could then go back to step two and ask for another single change. "Honey, could you try touching my whole breast?" Then, "Yessss . . . That's great." This helps both of you get better at defining your likes, wants, and desires in a nonblaming way.

Use It Everywhere

The use of this easy communication structure can take as many forms as you can think of for it. You'll use examples from the sensual and sexual context to practice it, but this style of communication can be used with your children, your boss, your employees, your friends, your mother, your neighbor, or your lover. By using it you'll be able to discover what you like and what you don't like and you'll empower your lover to freely give you what you want and ask for what they want too.

TIMING DURING LOVEMAKING

Getting creative with the timing of the positions you use during lovemaking will make all the difference in the quality of the experience. When you begin in certain postures and then move through to others, the woman begins to be aroused and the man can maintain his excitement without going over the top too soon. Learn to feel your way in this dance of love.

Arousal and Foreplay

The Kama Sutra and many other Asian love manuals from the past say that the woman's passions are slow to arousal. Once she is there though, she is hot and can often go beyond her partner in duration of the sex act. The great lover knows this and practices techniques to get her aroused and ready for each step in the lovemaking journey.

Many women don't feel empowered enough to educate their lovers on this fact. It's a very big reason that women loose interest in sex and go begrudgingly to the bedroom to fulfill their wifely duties. They aren't being aroused, have had a history of not being aroused, and can't find ways to step up to the plate to get what they need for arousal.

Timing of the Position Dance

Women need to help their men last longer so that they will enjoy every bit of the long, luxurious ride during intercourse. Don't think you are powerful and talented if you get him "off" too fast. That is not the point here.

Generally positions that put a lot of friction and stimulus on the *lingam* and *yoni* may be good for the woman to start intercourse in, but they won't be so great for the man unless he has mastered his ejaculation. Form a circle with your thumb and index finger with the fingertips touching. Now put the index finger of your other hand in and out of this circle. Notice that when you go straight in and out your fingers hardly touch.

Now, doing this same exercise, move your finger that is going in and out to an extreme angle – for example upward – so that the tip of that finger is pointing toward the fingers on the hand that is forming the circle. What happens? There's a lot more friction, isn't there? The friction is on the man's *lingam* and that friction is in just the right spot for the woman's G-spot.

Keep eye contact so that the two of you can be in communication, even if it isn't verbal at that moment.

Controlling Ejaculation

To last longer, try positions that give the man a lot of control in the movement of his pelvis. The Modified Yab/Yum Position where the man sits on the side of the bed or on a hassock and the woman sits on his lap, facing him, is good for ejaculation control and for hitting the G-spot in the woman. Another good one is for the woman to be lying back on the edge of the bed and the man to stand while he is inside of her. He can hold her legs or feet in the air or she can hold her own legs. This gives the man control over his timing and rhythm.

Relaxing positions, like the Spooning and Clasping Positions, are good for men who are trying to last longer. There's less friction and a relaxing mode is always helpful for control.

Timing of Orgasms

There are many types of orgasms and blends of orgasms, for both the man and the woman, but timing them so that everyone gets to have at least one is sometimes difficult. Creating the opportunity for the woman to have a clitoral orgasm first before intercourse is one way to accomplish this. Often this will lead to her being able to have a second or third vaginal orgasm during intercourse too.

Some men have a more difficult time having an orgasm than others. This is great for prolonged sex, but not very satisfying for the man who feels as though he can't let go into the orgasmic bliss. For this man, use positions that feel empowering and experiment with new, exciting positions too. Women, touch them lovingly and use your hands to brush the sexual energy into their heart area to remind them that they are loved and that they can relax and let go.

What's your favorite way to end a lovemaking experience? Ask your lover and each of you tell your favorite endings. Be descriptive and creative, but tell the truth. Try each other's suggestions out soon.

The ultimate is to have orgasms together, at the same time. This is something that is difficult for most couples and isn't necessary for lovemaking. Still, in the adventure of sex, it is something that can be easily accomplished if you are seasoned lovers and take the time to develop the capacity for it.

AFTER MAKING LOVE

The Kama Sutra suggests that the appropriate etiquette for the glow after making love is to bask in each other's arms and to speak words of love to each other. Caresses, kisses, and sweet wishes spoken to each other bring a sense of trust and warmth that is valuable to the emotional health of the couple.

Your memories are created and retained through your emotional reactions to what is happening. This is true for everything we do in life. Sweet emotional reactions are recorded in your memory and support positive response for the future.

CONNECTING THE HEART AND THE GENITALS

The Chinese art of lovemaking through the Taoist's perspective has an old saying that goes something like this: Women's energy comes from the heavens and moves to the earth and men's energy comes from the earth and moves towards the heavens. In other words – open a woman's heart first and then her legs will open; open a man's legs first and then his heart will open.

If we could all remember this and not take it personally when we are refused what we think we need, the world of men and women would work better. Each of us must move closer to the other's point of view and create ways to meet our needs. Create a dance of love between the two of you that shares the duties and the privileges of a wonderful sex life.

Creating more connection between the heart and the genitals can be easy. During sex, women can brush the sexual energy toward their lover's heart to remind them to feel the connection. Men can hold their lover in their arms and lightly touch their heart and their *yoni*. Put intention into your hearts for the healing of the differences.

INDEX

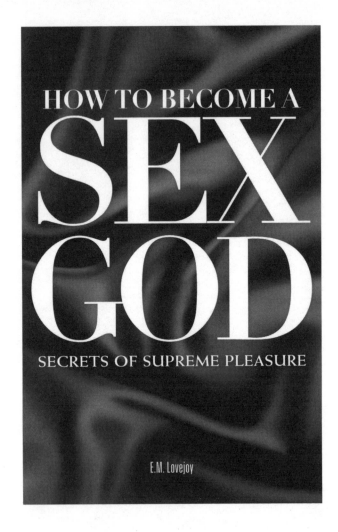

HOW TO BECOME A SEX GOD

SECRETS OF SUPREME PLEASURE

E.M. Lovejoy

£9.99
ISBN : 978-0-7153-3637-3